**ON YOUR FEET—
for a Mind-expanding Approach to Jogging!**

Tune-up to Total Awareness and enjoy every moment. Discover the inner secrets of liberating your body to reach the outer limits of vibrant health and dynamic self-confidence.

BEYOND JOGGING
THE INNER SPACES OF RUNNING

MIKE SPINO
DIRECTOR, ESALEN SPORTS CENTER

Introduction by Michael Murphy

A BERKLEY MEDALLION BOOK
published by
BERKLEY PUBLISHING CORPORATION

Celestial Arts
231 Adrian Road
Millbrae, CA 94030

Library of Congress Catalog Card Number 75-28771

SBN 425-03348-1

*BERKLEY MEDALLION BOOKS are published by
Berkley Publishing Corporation
200 Madison Avenue
New York, N.Y. 10016*

BERKLEY MEDALLION BOOK ® TM 757,375

Printed in the United States of America

Berkley Medallion Edition, MARCH, 1977

CONTENTS

To Louie, Buddy, Glen, Joey and Pete, Mom and Dad, Sis and Uncle Frank, Coach Cippolla and Coach Ruggiero and many others in my hometown of Lyndhurst, New Jersey.

Toward an Integral Training

Many cultures have recognized a profound connection between sport, philosophy and religion. The relation between games and the holy, between body and spirit, has been celebrated in the ancient Greek Olympiad, in the Irish sacred games, in the rituals of Tibet, in *Tapa Wanka Yap* — a game of the Sioux in which God's grace and omnipresence were revealed to the players, in the Mayan ballgame and in the martial arts of China and Japan. In modern times, however, most of the connection has been lost. Religious games have vanished in the secular West.

But in recent years there has been a movement to reestablish the bridge between sport and the further reaches of mind and spirit. Famous athletes practice hypnosis and meditation. Clinics are held on the "inner game" of tennis. Tai Chi and Yoga appear in physical education courses. Martial Arts are enjoying a world-wide renascence. Mike Spino's integral training springs from this reawakening and makes an original contribution, I think, to the coaching of middle and long distance runners.

I speak at first hand, for Mike has coached me during the last two years—has led me through an ordeal and adventure that has produced a 4:40 1500 meters, a respectable marathon and a three-mile downhill run in twelve minutes and thirty seconds. By combining imaginative approaches to mind and spirit with good physical fundamentals he has turned me and many others into running enthusiasts, addicts it may be admitted. His approach draws from some of the best ancient and modern techniques, both mental and physical. It is, I think, on the mainline to the athletic training of the future.

Michael Murphy

BEYOND JOGGING

CHAPTER I

Running to a Different Drummer

Many Americans have taken up jogging in the past 10 years. Late in the afternoon on almost any day, San Francisco's Marina green near the Golden Gate Bridge is a moving tide of runners. Frequently I stop to watch them. I'm amazed at how many run the same distance at the same pace for months on end. Whether they are running hard or shuffling along slowly few of them seem to reflect any transcendence in what they are doing. It seems more an obligation than a joy. At least a third of these runners could improve more quickly and enjoy running more if they knew a variety of gaits and tempos; they could bring new insight into what they are doing through visualization and meditation. I see running as an art form as well as a means of physical conditioning. But information that could help the daily jogger has been reserved largely for a few competitive athletes. My purpose is to combine these techniques with the self-awareness attitudes that have been brought to public attention by the human potential movement. A blending of the power of body and mind can carry us to new plateaus of creative achievement.

There are physiological reasons why running is more rewarding than the customary jogging. But my purpose goes beyond the physiological; my purpose is to help you to release your own inner meanings, to run to the drummer that is *you*.

The jogging fad that hit America came partly from the enormous success of a group of New Zealand athletes who, following the training of Arthur Lydiard, set new world records using long distance running as the main tool of their training regimen. This marathon type running came to be known in the United States as LSD, Long Slow Distance. Although marathon running is the main thrust of Lydiard's system, there are detailed suggestions for running up and down hills to improve speed conditioning, and a system for race practice. His overall philosophy as outlined in his book, *Run to the Top,* is often neglected by those who assume his successes —Peter Snell, Murray Halberg, Bill Baille and others—came from plodding runs through the New Zealand countryside.

After helping the Mexican government prepare its athletes for the 1968 Olympic Games, Lydiard toured the United States, and his enthusiasm did much to promote jogging. It also rigidified LSD, then a new form of athletic training. I have run my fastest marathon using long slow running, but I had 12 years of speed training behind me. And, I also had Bob Deines, a former American 50-mile champion, as my morning running mate.

I do not subscribe to an exclusively LSD approach because I've found that those who lean on it run in packs and never seem to have meaningful experiences. It also seems that in some training groups the beginners fall behind and never have a chance to find identity in running. Better to do your own 50-yard tempos and gaits. In this way you are working toward realization of your own potential.

My obsession with running (and I admit it is an a obsession) began when I was a teenager. While in high school I was a champion runner, clocking a 4:22 mile. At Syracuse University I set the mile and two-mile records. Since then, running has continued to be a major part of my life. My running time is my thinking time, my art form.

After graduation from college I studied with two of the world's greatest maverick coaches, both of them authorities in middle and distance running. They were Australia's Percy Wells Cerutty, whom I call the mystic renegade, and Hungarian-born Mihaly Igloi, who gave running an important new language to help communicate technique. When I had the privilege of studying under these two powerful and somewhat eccentric men I was able to compare their methods with the standard practices of track coaches. I found the Cerutty and Igloi techniques to be so far superior to the training I had had in high school and college that I decided to try to pass their wisdom on to others.

I found that their methods could be blended into a training program suitable not only for the aspiring racer and over-40 marathon runner but for men and women of all ages and capacities who realize the importance of regular exercise.

This new training program is divided into three parts: 65% for improving endurance, 25% for developing tempo or speed, and 10% resistance training to build body strength. Aerobic endurance (or stamina) training builds muscle tone and strengthens the cardiovascular system, just as jogging does. For this we use slow tempos and loose gaits. Anaerobic tempo (or speed) training is to increase the body's ability to use oxygen. It is also known as oxygen debt training. The final 10% of the training is to develop muscle and skeletal power, putting the body into stress by means of hills or sand dunes that force the body into exertion. I also use isometric body tension exercises and workouts with light and heavy weights.

For the beginner this discipline is intended as a means to health and expansion of capacities. For the would-be champion the training methods described can offer a way to surpass his present attainments. Running has to be your own thing. Run with a soul mate if you can, but learn to float, accelerate, gallop, canter and relax while running. Experience fine-tuned breathing. Run to your own drummer. If you choose to go LSD with someone, make sure they possess the kind of personality that will benefit you spiritually as well as physically. Better yet, make sure they know some poetry or can sing!

Jogging Can Be Hazardous to Your Health

Jogging is not the most efficient form of running if you want to become physically fit. It might even be hazardous to your mind and spirit. Some joggers have their own special way of being in the world. These few, somewhat like Zen students sitting zazen, may gain access to self-knowledge through the constant repitition of the jog. But, if you find that your psyche cannot stop plodding through life, if all your running is only jogging, you may become both physically fit and stodgy.

This might sound like treason coming from a running fanatic like me, but it hurts to see a potentially beautiful expression like running end up a jogging trend which creates ruts on grass fields. In the late afternoon, across America, you can see dozens of people lock-stepping their way around parks and track ovals—it's almost as if they punch themselves through from 9 to 5 and continue the same compulsive obsession from 5:30 to 6. Jogging reminds me of the routine work ethic. When the same tasks are done over and over again we seek distractions. We begin living for the next coffee break; our spirit loses its freshness and nothing new or spontaneous seems to happen.

Jogging is one-dimensional, the same motion repeated over and over again. Play denotes diversity, its spice is change and variety. Jogging can be like working on an assembly line. You may finish the daily ordeal with a vague sense of satisfaction and a dull feeling of regret.

My profession as a physical fitness counselor puts me in contact with many people who have increased their jogs from one lap to five. At this point, if not before, many become bored and suffer real and psychosomatic problems. Some continue to do their laps while others quit, become defensive about it, and remain in awe of those who continue and seem able to put up with the boredom.

There is good news for those who continue and for those who would like to begin. There can be more to improving your cardiovascular condition than jogging—you can run. When you run there is a diversity of possible movements, and a possible joy. Each run does not produce special experiences, but finding the right teacher or running partner can increase the chances of transforming running from a routine act into a physical and spiritual surprise.

In the Spring of 1973 Esalen Institute created a center to explore the possibilites of sport and human growth. I became associated with the Center, and Michael Murphy, founder and guiding force of Esalen, and I became running partners and each other's student. I began learning about meditation and eastern religions from him, and Murphy made the commitment to attempt to run the mile in less than six minutes. Michael was 43, had never run in his life, but possessed a 'young' body with light bones in relation to his body structure. He had the type of concentration that seems to go with meditation. Through our conversations I began to realize that running was a form of meditation, and that some of my experiences while running were similar to those described in the esoteric yogic literature. Michael told me of his teacher, Sri Aurobindo, of the possibilities for bringing energies of mind, what he termed *Supermind,* down into the body.

The challenge of helping Murphy prepare for the under-six-minute mile brought to the surface the information I had gained from my association with Milhay Igloi, and Percy Wells Cerutty. From Igloi's lore I taught Michael the importance of tempo running, the subtle differences between aerobic and anaerobic metabolism, and the utilization of short interval runs. I tried, as Cerutty taught, to view athletics as an artistic expression. We experimented with the gaits of movement: the amble, trot, canter, and gallop. After three months Murphy ran a 5:45 mile, and 18 months after that placed third in the Western Regional Master's (over 40) pentathlon championship. During this performance he recorded a 4:47 1,500 meters, the best for any competitor including all the 30 to 39 year old pentathaletes.

There is a body of technique which enables an individual to diversify his or her running. Instead of constant jogging, I prescribe a mixed formula for the beginning runner which includes 65 percent endurance, 25 percent speed or tempo and 10 percent resistance training. These percentages are based on a quota of time, effort, and distance run. These runs include various techniques. The Chinese shuffle is a way of running in which your awareness is concentrated below the knees with the foot plant on the heels. Another run, fresh swing tempo, is executed by lifting the knee and stepping out in a cyclical action between 20 to 40 percent effort. There is also a way to surge for 25 yards by pressing the thumb and first finger together while making a 'bing' sound in the larynx and expelling the body forward.

What I do cannot be termed *jogging*. It is a way of *running* in which to evoke a spirit and sense of possibility. This spirit becomes manifested in numerous ways, some planned, others quite spontaneous. For instance, there is a run I often take from the Saint Frances Yacht Harbor, (San Francisco) skirting the waterfront out to the Golden Gate Bridge. It is a run to be done a thousand times without repeating the experience. Half way into the four-mile run I stop at a precipice overlooking the sea and look for omens. What vessel in the sea, what ocean color, what tide will show the day's meaning? I often run the four miles in what the Swedes term *fartlek* or "speed play." By varying my gait and speed, by lightening or increasing my tempo, I vary my metabolism and shift the mood. As the run progresses I become speechless and shift my speeds as the momentum takes me. Often at dusk, on an early fall day, the run brings tears to my eyes.

The innerspaces which the mind experiences while running this way is close to meditation. As you become fit, the mind has more chance for expansion. I have experimented with the transference of meditation consciousness to running. I do this by practicing the observation of thought. I might meditate for five minutes this way and then run for 15 minutes. I might repeat the process three or four times, going deeper into my consciousness while at the same time seeming to abandon the body. Once during a run I voyaged from remembering the sounds and smells of my grandfather's house to a sense of watching my body from a place above myself. But my main objective is to test our limits by using running as a way to self understanding. The quest of spirit through the body has just begun.

CHAPTER II

Training the Competitive Runner: Percy Wells Cerutty and Mihaly Igloi

"Watch children run and go and do likewise."
Percy Wells Cerutty

Percy Wells Cerutty was perhaps the most dramatic personality to emerge in the running world during the 1950s. While most American and European coaches were plotting schedules to break the four-minute mile, Cerutty was leading his runners up sand dunes, making them run barefoot on the beach(as he did), and listen to inspirational music (as he did). To this Johnny-come-lately in the field of competitive running the sport was an outpouring, a giving of oneself. No other teacher before him had ever expressed running in mystical terms. At

---

*Many of the quotes in this chapter come from a small phamplet, "Running with Cerutty," published by *Track and Field News* in 1959. All of Cerutty's written works are out of print and the pamphlet is something of a collector's item passed on to me by a fellow runner. Cerutty's aim for the past 10 years was to share his ideas with the general public. "Humanity," he called it.

first he was ridiculed, but later admired as his athletes chalked up 30 world records.

Cerutty was a key figure during the quest for the first four-minute mile. He coached John Landy and later guided Herb Elliott in his fabulous career. He motivated Dave Stephens and Albert Thomas to world record-breaking times. His influence changed Australia from an athletically backward nation into an international leader in distance running. He was a pioneer, and he started first with himself.

It was 40 years ago that Cerutty, then a sickly 43-year-old, transformed himself into a wiry, vital athletic teacher. He brought a whole new world of thought to the training curriculum. An original thinker regarding body movement, he was a motivator as well. Motivation came in the form of a new freedom he gave to running. As his fame grew, his training camp at Portsea, Australia, became a migratory station for aspiring champions.

To those still anchored to the belief that athletes should run all-out every day until they were exhausted, Cerutty's ideas were entirely revolutionary. "There should be nothing inhibited, regimented, formalized, fixed or dictated in running," he wrote at the time. His insight came from watching the effortless gallops of children and animals. He analyzed the way the body moved while running and became convinced that upper body strength was crucial to high athletic performance. But he also had another strange idea: that running begins in the hands and fingers.

"I believe the fixed, immovable elbow and the swaying shoulders are the two most common faults in runners. When used as they should be, the arms and hands initiate the drives that vary both the pace and the effort," he said. "The consciousness should be moved to the upper body, the back, arms and fingers and the drive initiated in these parts, the legs following on. From this it follows that if the movements above the hips are not perfect we cannot expect perfect movements in the legs and feet.

Although Cerutty was training world record-breakers with this philosophy nearly 20 years ago, most coaches and physical education instructors to this day do not incorporate such advanced ideas in training. Although volumes have been written about training systems in relation to distances to be run and the development of speed, little has appeared in print about the body's movement when running.

Cerutty was also the first to turn a new lens on the placement of the foot while running. Perhaps because he ran barefoot on the beaches of Portsea and could feel very keenly how the foot falls naturally, he disclaimed the then-popular method of making contact first with the ball of the foot, before dropping down on the heel. "The outer edge of the foot makes contact first and the middle edge drops down in a movement designed by nature to prevent jar," he observed. Upon leaving the ground the toes come into action and grip with their little pads. The camera shows us that the foot approaches the ground with toes cocked up as if it was to be a heel landing. In very slow motion it can be viewed as a slow slither with a caressing movement from the outside of the whole foot to the inside, embodying a clamp-down movement much as we use to stamp a coin rolling to the gutter.

Cerutty's keen observations throughout his life proved useful to him as a coach. His highly original concept of varying gaits for runners originated from a childhood spent around horses and stables. He adapted animal movements for training. He added more fertile ideas by watching the incredible stamina and stride of Australian aborigines.

Breathing

Tidal breathing was another Percy original. Using a rhythm in which the inhalations and exhalations correspond to ocean waves, his runners were able to both accelerate and rest during motion. As the air comes into the body the drive is off; on the exhalation the breath is expelled from the abdomen and released with a sound from the larynx. Arms and hands move up

nd down with the tidal movement, allowing for alternating
est and drive, rest and drive.

Other of Cerutty's theories have gone through stages,
such as his ideas on arm carriage and running style. It was not
until 1959 when Herb Elliott toured the United States that his
mentor was asked to summarize his ideas on the upper body
during running. Here is what Cerutty said:

1. *Down thrust in warming up.*   The arms are forced
igorously down as if driving the body upward as they go.
This movement tends to ensure that the body is well uplifted
before actual hard running commences.

2. *The throw-away pickup.*   These movements, used as
rest or break (especially in preparing to run fast as in
arming up) are as if something was carried, thrown away and
icked up again. A yoyo is a good illustration. The use of this
movement prepares the mind to reject the burdens or logs that
s thrust upon it by hard effort.

3. *The low-carriage full-spring action.*   This is the
normal full throw of the arms used by good sprinters when
unning fast. The arms or hands start from a line that parallels
he side seam of the running shorts. When down in this
position the arm is nearly straight. The arms are then thrown
igorously upward and outward across to a point that corresponds in space with a line drawn down the center of the trunk
and level with the mouth.

4. *The crawl movement.*   This is a natural and early
orm of movement that corresponds to the crawl of a child or
he dog paddle of elementary swimming. It is the earliest of
movements and little used.

5. *The rest position.*   The arms rest high on the chest
with little movement and thus the body "coasts" for a few
strides before the arms are dropped and you pick up the drive.

In later years Cerutty stylized his teaching method using
erms that corresponded to horses gaits. He called these basic
movements the stretch, the amble, the trot, the canter and the
gallop. The *amble* loosens the upper body, freeing the shoul-

ders. The *trot* is a bit faster. The *canter* is asymmetrical, with steps of different lengths. The *gallop* has the same movements as the canter but is carried out with more vigor and further reaching of the arms. Cerutty claimed the motion corresponded to the natural energies of the body and that this stylized formula allows a person to run competitively with the same freedom as primitive man did.

In 1974 while Cerutty was in the United States for a series of workshops and lectures sponsored by the Esalen Sports Center, he outlined the basic tenets for full lung aeration (FLA) and more natural animal-like movements. They appear here for the first time:

1. Say to yourself, *"shoulders,"* and practice lifting the shoulders so that the air will come into the lungs under atmospheric pressure.

2. Expel the air fast, by throwing down one arm as it reaches out. But the body musn't drop; only the arm, thrown out and down.

3. A natural noise should accompany the exhalation. This noise, from the larnyx, confirms the expelling of the air and removes all tension in the body since the epiglottis is the point of tension. No muscle can move as fast as it should if no noise comes from the throat.

4. Watch that the head is not back on the shoulders or sticking out in front.

Because Cerutty believed there is too little emphasis on torso strength and too much emphasis on power in the legs he stresses strength or resistance training. Strength training, he says, enables the athlete to move his concentration from the legs, which are "inferior" to the trunk and its organs which are "superior."

"I am convinced," he told me, "that for future superior performance, running alone can never be the answer. Strength, *added* strength, by means of the gymnasium, the barbell, the sand dune, steep hill, grass or road, or by means of flights of stairs in the cities is needed to add resistance to training.

"A certain amount of steady, continuing effort is required to strengthen the heart and acquire good oxygen debt. But resistance, putting the musculature through a series of efforts against resistance, is a requirement often overlooked in athletic conditioning."

Cerutty, who died in 1975 at the age of 80, practiced both weight training and distance running to some remarkable athletic achievements. When he was 51, he ran a hundred miles in 24 hours and was the Victoria marathon champion. At age 65 he gave weight lifting exhibitions in Melbourne. He credited his success to the combination of resistance training and distance running.

In resistance training, progress is achieved only by increasing the amount of resistance as you go along. For this reason he advised against the use of light weights that body builders use, claiming they make for bulk, not strength. He preferred weights that can be lifted six times without undue stress but that are difficult or impossible to lift ten times. The one exception: the dead lift with a weight that can be lifted at least 20 times but not as much as 30.

Cerutty recommended the use of the following exercises regularly:

1. The snatch, using one third of the body weight. Ten repetitions.

2. Rowing motion, six to ten repetitions, three sets of repetitions for 18 to 30 in all.

3. The press, the curl (front and reverse) and the one-handed swing, all six to ten repetitions and three sets, 18 to 30 in all.

4. The dead lift, 20 to 30 repetitions, three sets.

Cerutty also builds strength through uphill running, wrestling, chin-ups, sit-ups and push-ups.

How to Develop Power

"All-over organism power:heart-lungs-glands-muscle-spirit power" is the philosophy Cerutty used to guide those under his watchful eyes. It was part of Cerutty's genius that he looked at running and other athletic achievements as more than a simple pastime. He encouraged his students to bring all their mental powers to bear on their chosen sport. He probed into the psyche of the athlete, coupling innate brainpower and will with the innate running ability of the animal. This combination resulted in techniques that lifted his students above the ordinary.

It was said by Herb Elliott, Cerutty's most accomplished pupil, that 90 percent of what he learned from Cerutty had nothing to do with techniques or physical principles. In Portsea, there is a vault in which Percy kept certain writings, saved for the day the athlete needs a special lift for a sup⸱ ative effort. Cerutty would bring them out just b⸱ ⸱ an event. They dealt with the origins of the univ⸱ ⸱⸱, man's place in the evolution of the species, and the need for a revolution in life-style if the world is to survive. The morning before a major event, Cerutty would take his student to a park near the stadium area and, as the athlete ran, Cerutty nearby perform⸱ l a ritual of running himself to exhaustion. It was said that⸱ ⸱e foamed from the mouth after an exhausting sessio⸱⸱ ⸱ would tell the athlete, "You may run faster today, bu⸱ ⸱ou will not run harder."

With this ritual, Cerutty believe⸱1 ⸱⸱⸱ athlete reached the proper mental state to perform later ⸱⸱ the stadium; no one was allowed to talk to the athlete from this time till the race. He might sleep or do some light reading, but if a newsman or photographer chanced to come around he had to deal with Cerutty. The athlete even rested by the side of the track until the call for the race. At that time Cerutty motioned the athlete to the starting line, and he was on his own to perform at his best.

And As For Food

In the days when the science of nutrition was in its adolescence Cerutty believed that proper diet could make a difference in athletic performance. In his rather unusual style, he wrote, "I value most highly the food that is fed to the human organism. That I value above training [exercise]."

He could be classified as a lacto-vegetarian. He knew that overcooking eliminated what he called the "life principle" in food and made it "dead food." Rather, he believed that hard food is best: raw rolled oats with dried fruits such as raisins and nuts, walnuts and bananas. At his training camp in Portsea, the "proper foods" he served included thinly sliced potatoes fried in vegetable oil, baked beans, lightly poached eggs, fish, whole wheat bread with peanut butter, treacle, honey and jams. He avoided white sugar, flour, butter or tea, or any fluid with meals.

The standard lunch at Portsea was the "comprehensive salad," served at every noon meal every day of the year. It included fruit, vegetables, tinned fish, tongue, mild cheeses, hard-boiled eggs and an oil and lemon dressing. Whole wheat bread accompanied it.

Dinner was equally healthful and usually included a thick soup (shank broth with barley was a favorite), followed by steamed or baked fish or poultry, sliced potatoes fried in oil and lightly steamed vegetables in season.

The taboos that evolved over the years at the Cerutty table are rather simple and by today's standards do not seem dogmatic or cultish. Animal fats in any form are taboo. Vegetable oils replaced butter or lard. No cakes or biscuits were allowed as snacks. And while no liquid was consumed with the meal, as much as you liked could be drunk two hours after the meal and up to the next meal time. Alcohol was accepted only in moderation. Tobacco was banned. He relied on extra intake of vitamins B, C, and E.

Although Cerutty had fixed ideas on diet and training, he was basically non-authoritarian in contrast to Igloi. His attitude, I think, accounts for his success as a coach of Olympic and world record holders. "I teach the athlete to become self-dependent, to determine his own schedules, and to become an efficient mental and physical organism as soon as possible,'' he said. He did not have the fatherly need some coaches do of having their students dependent on them.

While Igloi, whom you will meet next, adhered to fixed schedules, Cerutty's aim was to give athletes principles of fitness. He taught style, and innovative ways to approach running. He was the first to stress the importance of awareness and consciousness of the self in the sport: ''A runner must think inward. Like a dancer who learns intricate steps at first he must study himself, actually look down at his own movements, check up on himself in mirrors.''

There was no total philosophical system: rather, Cerutty relied on concepts based on his own observations and experiences and he delivered them in bits and pieces as we ran over sand dunes and beaches. In this way he was a prime mover, a motivator. According to Bill Emmerton, who has run more recorded miles than any man in history, and Albert Thomas, a former world record holder in the two-mile, Percy's great genius was to motivate and inspire. While traditional athletic teaching has nothing to do with becoming a whole person (witness the number of high school and college students who give up athletics after their school days), Percy Wells Cerutty joined practical athletics with spiritual ideas and ideals. This attention to the whole person was a major inspiration to those in training with him and moved them to great achievements.

''Every difficulty carries within itself the means of its own solution.'' ''The test for you is to find that means, that teacher. There is a teacher at every crossroad in life. You never know that until you reach the crossroad. He is not available while you are on the journey to his place in life.''

''Running as I teach it is not a sport or physical activity so much as a complete expression of ourselves, physical, mental, and spiritual. Running as I teach it is the full and complete development of the athlete.''

It was just this mystical quality that first drew me to him. My faith in him was strengthened by his recognition of the importance of the spontaneous and the instinctive. "Every situation requires an instinctive response," he said. "We cannot act every moment in conscious thought. A person with a high degree of cell fitness and mind development will have unconscious reaction to every situation that is superior to those who are not so well-endowed physically or intellectually."

When Cerutty visited the United States in 1974, he used my house as basecamp for his workshops and lectures. Since he was then 79, most people expected a mellow man who could deliver the word. But Percy was outrageous. He ranted and raved and yelled from the moment he rose until he fell asleep at night. He was on a coiled spring. Nobody expected this and I found myself an apologist for him. Not many can tolerate his style.

But those of us who knew him and lived with him and ran with him could forgive his rages because we knew he was warm and sincere and offered a rare comradery. His work is like a cosmic leap into all that is alive and magical in athletics, and knowing him gave meaning to our lives beyond mere physical attainment.

Mihaly Igloi

Another inventive running coach entered the arena of world competition during the renaissance of track and field sports in the 1950s. He was Mihaly Igloi, whose outstanding work in physical fitness with Hungarian soldiers drew him into the world spotlight. Under his aegis, Hungary produced the leading distance runners in the world.

In the mid-fifties, Igloi immigrated to the United States and as coach of the Santa Clara Youth Village and the Los Angeles Track Club he became the most successful track coach in the history of American distance running. He devised a running method that surpassed all others.

"You can always tell an Igloi runner," says a colleague who has trained under this irascible Hungarian. Igloi's pupils are so smooth in their style they seem to be propelled on wheels. Their stride, in fact, is cyclical and relies on the lift of the knee and a shortened step to burst over the ground, outdistancing the long-striding competitor. Igloi's system of interval training, which he adapted from several sources, was responsible for building the remarkable muscle power that took his athletes to the top in world competition.

Igloi was initially influenced in his training methods by the great German athlete Rudolph Harbig. Then, at the 1936 Olympics, Igloi adopted the interval system which he later used with great success. When running intervals, the athlete divides running distances, from 60 yards to one mile, into segments which he runs at varying speeds and tempos. A variation is classical interval training in which the distance run and the rest periods are of equal length. During the 1940s, Gosta Holmer, a Swedish coach, further varied interval training with *fartlek* or "speed play," in which the Swedes would run on pine needle paths, changing their rhythm spontaneously. In this way the interval runs were transferred from the track to the natural environment and the run and rest periods were chosen at random.

Using *fartlek*, Swedes Arne Anderson and Gunder Haeg ran 4:01 miles for the first time. Igloi adapted the interval and *fartlek* systems into a method run entirely on the track and adjacent grassy areas. He created a language for various types of running and prescribed individual formulas for his runners. The intervals were not spontaneous, but Igloi believed the method was more scientific than *fartlek*. It was during the 1954-55 season that his methods came to international attention.

The Method

Igloi's method is based on tempo, on leg movement, length of step and on reserving power for the maximum effort needed during a race. He stressed upper lobe or surface breathing from the chest, not the abdomen. He relied on the commitment that his students would eat, drink and sleep running under his prescribed plan. They put between 80 and 150 miles a week on their track shoes. During workouts when as many as 50 people would be running back and forth upon the grass or track, Igloi would give instructions individually, changing each person's intervals daily based on his personal observations. He seemed like a doctor giving advice, a cure, without telling you what the trouble was. Acutely analytical, he relied on his superb sensing device to dictate workout patterns. He never wrote anything down; his techniques remain even today locked within him. This book is the first attempt to publish his remarkable system.

The Igloi system is based on runs of from 60 to 440 yards. Each run is made at a specific speed that he calls *tempo*. The swing tempo and its variations is a motion in which you extend your leg, lift the knee and step out in a cyclical action. Using his language: fresh swing tempo, good swing tempo, hard swing tempo. *Fresh swing tempo* is a floating action in which as little effort as possible is exerted. It is the tempo for beginning a race, and in training it is interspersed for relaxation and for recovery after harder efforts with faster speeds.

Good swing tempo is the leg action used most frequently. One uses the same cyclical action of the leg as in fresh swing tempo but at medium effort. *Hard swing tempo* is a driving action with long strides such as might be made on the third lap of a mile run.

Igloi's notion of speed running is based on his belief that acceleration is best accomplished by short, staccato steps rather than long strides. Short steps have always been a technique of marathon runners, but track coaches tend to emphasize long, driving steps at the acceleration point in middle distances. In Igloi's speed tempo the steps are shortened, the foot plant is just behind the toes and the arms are held high with the elbows pointed slightly outward. ("You can

always tell a Igloi runner.'') The arms give balance and help establish a rhythm. Breathing is surface, in the upper lobes of the lungs. *Good speed* is medium acceleration; *hard speed* is about 70 per cent effort, and *all out* is "what you can." Many times there is a build-up of speed from one tempo to the next.

Igloi rarely timed runs; he stressed effort and technique above time. His ego was such that he firmly believed athletes who followed his commands and specifications would reach their goals: Speed came with practice, not from being timed. Endurance developed from running many miles at a slow pace rather than from fast sprints, he said in his stormy Hungarian manner.

Yet the problem of balance remained. Too much emphasis on distance running without timing and sprinting could siphon off the zest for training. Too much fast running, on the other hand, can cause euphoria that leads the runner to neglect endurance training. It was Igloi's genius to tap into an athlete's natural cycles of emotional, physical and mental states. He noticed his students might train exceptionally well one day and have great difficulty duplicating the same effort the following day. He found this to be so disconcerting to his runners that he stopped timing them at all until his interval training at various levels conditioned them to peak fitness. He compares training for peak performance the same as "learning to be the first violinist in the finest concert orchestra in the world."

Critics of Igloi say he does not prepare the individual for the rigors of international competition because none of his world record holders have ever won an Olympic gold medal. It could be that his authoritarianism ("do it my way") and his tempermental outbursts destroy the athlete's ability to make the split-second decisions necessary in top class running. But for my money, his conditioning tools enhance health, fitness and awareness of the body's capabilities over long distances.

I'll never forget the day in 1966 that I arrived in Southern California to train with him. I had first read about him several years before in an article in *Look* magazine. I had run well in

Syracuse, New York, but the weather in Syracuse wasn't suitable to year-round training and that, along with philosophical conflicts with the coaching staff, persuaded me to seek out Igloi and train for the four-minute mile. I had been a distance runner in a high school that had no distance training program and had run 4:22 mile there. Later, at Syracuse, I set a school record with a 4:09 mile. It was time to move on.

On my arrival from New York I hitchhiked from the airport to Santa Monica City College where Igloi trained the Santa Monica Athletic Association team. When I got to the training area I was so eager to join the forty or fifty people I saw running in every direction I just vaulted over the fence. Some of the outstanding runners of the year were there—Ron Larrieu, Norm Higgins, Tracy Smith—all running in different directions near the track. Few were actually running on the track and most were running in what seemed to be a random, patternless manner. It was bedlam, or so it seemed to a 20-year-old used to the clocked instructions of a coach. On closer observation, however, I saw they knew what they were doing.

Later, when I knew him better, he would explain his theory this way, comparing his ideas to the wires in a radio. "The novice has all the wires but he doesn't know where they should go," he said. He told stories of world class athletes who had come to train with him and after hard running effort at a slow pace wanted to quit for the day. Igloi would recommend a series of interval runs and the athlete's momentum returned. He could then resume running after these intervals whereas before he had been totally spent.

It is this combination of various intervals and tempos that mark Igloi's great contribution to distance training. It is difficult to master and it takes daily practice. Another important aspect is that Igloi could balance students' workouts so that they received equal amounts of speed and endurance training up to their maximum capacity. Most coaches are familiar with the two states the body can enter while running:

aerobic (cardiovascular) and anaerobic (oxygen debt) states.

In the aerobic state the body tires but the athlete is not too out of breath to hold a conversation with a fellow runner. An anaerobic oxygen debt state, on the other hand, is when the body cannot supply enough oxygen for its accelerated needs and the runner pants for breath. The miler gasping for the finish or the runner leaning over to inhale deeply are examples of the body experiencing oxygen debt. The legs might feel strong but the lungs cannot breathe deeply enough. It is the subtle blending of training methods to increase stamina (aerobic training) and to increase the ability to use oxygen (anaerobic) that made Igloi's methods a breakthrough in training programs.

To illustrate the complexity and the variety of interval training, here is a typical workout.

Typical Workout for a 25-year-old Athlete
Training for a 4-Minute Mile

6:30 A.M.

Jog 5 large laps—about 2½ miles
Fifteen times 100-yard shake-ups
Six 220s on the grass with a 220 interval between each at good swing tempo
Four 220s, good speed on the track
Six 220s on the grass at good swing tempo
Three 330s on grass at fresh swing with 110 rest between each
One 260 on track, all out
Ten 100-yard shake-ups

4:00 P.M.

Jog three large laps—about 1 mile
Ten 100-yard shake-ups
Six 110 yards, good speed accelerating to 70 percent effort

Three sets of four 440s between 59-61 seconds with 220 rest
    between each run. Five minutes between each set
Five 330s, fresh swing tempo on grass
Six 100s, all out on grass with no interval
Ten 100-yard shake-ups

This workout would take 3 hours in the morning and in the
afternoon. It is an average day's training. A 3- or 6-miler
would train about 4½ hours with not as much speed. You
would run between 14-18 miles on this day.

    The body undergoes subtle changes with each variation in
conditioning; everyone's body reacts differently according to
the physical condition of the athlete and the cycle of training
he is performing at that particular stage. For contrast, compare
it to the classical interval system in which the athlete runs only
one distance and then has a timed or jogged rest. In Igloi's
system the rest periods are changed in each part of the set. You
might have six or seven different periods of rest during a
two-hour workout. While it is a complicated system that can
be thoroughly absorbed only by apprenticeship, it is worth
passing on.

    To give you an idea of what it was like to train with Igloi,
let me describe a typical day's training. Picture a warm
California sun and, yes, a bit of smog. There might be 40 to 50
people working out on and around the track and grassy field.
During my stay the group included an 11-year-old girl who ran
12 miles a day, businessmen, women athletes and housewives,
college students and international class athletes. Each was on
an individual Igloi program and the ten-year veteran was
treated with the same fatherly concern as the jogger.

    Put yourself in that scene. You might warm up with ten
long, slow laps, followed by shake-ups. Shake-ups are a
relaxation method in which you jog while allowing all your
muscles to land loosely on the skeleton. Shake-ups are used

before and after a workout. By dropping your arms and letting your body bounce you are able to relax to the point where fast running can follow immediately. It is a method of getting your body and mind into the right space for a power effort. I have seen athletes run hard after ten shake-ups where another would have to run four or five 100-yard sprints to achieve the same preparation.

After the shake-ups you might run 220 yards at fresh swing tempo, alternating each 220 yards with a 220 rest (walk or jog) in between. This could be followed by running four 110-yard distances with 50-yard rests between each. Finally you might run 260 yards four times on the track at hard speed. (This group of intervals is called a "set.") It might be followed by one long, slow lap before you start on another set of different runs and rests. Igloi gave only one set at a time, ⸱⸱⸱ ⸱⸱serving the runner's response, for the response could result in a change in the rest of the day's schedule…somewhat like the quarterback changing a particular play at the line of scrimmage.

One day Igloi gave me a set of ten 100-yard dashes on the grass section inside the track. I was to run each 100 all out with no rest period, simply turning around and heading back. Half way through I realized it was a specific kind of test. I ran them all out from the first step, and by the sixth interval I had reached such an oxygen debt that I could be heard groaning throughout the stadium. When I finished I fell to the grass in exhaustion, as much mental as physical. Igloi came over and said, "When the mind says *yes* the body obeys." He took such performances matter-of-factly as though he were a scientist watching a rat perform in a maze.

A single afternoon workout could last four hours. In addition there was always the morning 90-minute run. We never finished until late in the evening. It was a dawn to dusk life in the out-of-doors and I don't think I have ever experienced the seasons as I did that year.

Although I never ran a 4:00 mile I felt that I gained tremendously in training techniques that I could pass on to others. Eventually, of course, it was time to leave. I felt much like a chrysalis, both protected and awakened. There were moments we had that I wouldn't trade... the early summer, with Igloi in shirt sleeves jumping and dancing in ecstasy as we bombed quarter after quarter over the cinders...and the rainy days when we slogged through the wet grass and he stayed, even though everyone else had gone home, even though he knew we would finish the workout without him. But he wanted to be there, despite the weather, to share it. And when the team was done and shuffled into the locker room he'd come and mimic how we ran, put us all into a reverie with his fatherly love as he told us to jog a few laps and go home.

CHAPTER III

An Integral Training Program

gging is not enough. In a society that seeks new paradigms
many aspects of living, the goal for the athlete is to offer a
w model of creativity and insight through sport. Running
ers increased vitality and awareness; it is my yoga and from
 have found new energy for the requirements of my daily
. Others tell me that running helps overcome depression,
blize the appetite, help control weight, and just makes them
l better. A run before breakfast is a fine tune-up for a day's
rk, especially if you have an office job. A run after work
ars the cobwebs of fatigue from the mind for more thorough
joyment of family activities.

Until recently, few athletes publicly acknowledged that,
 them, sport was a kind of yoga. In the workshops I lead in
n Francisco and Big Sur, California, the whole purpose is to
 beyond jogging, to expand awareness of the joys of running
d push our bodies to new limits of achievement for physical
d mental fitness. We begin by winnowing away our pre-
nceptions about running and looking at the subject with
sh eyes. We strive to run more naturally, like animals: we

trot, gallop, and canter, using the upper body for forwar
thrust. By combining these running tempos and strides wi
visualization and meditation, new patterns of thought surfa
and we move toward a richer mind-body experience. Athlet
in years to come will benefit from the ground broken by t
human potential movement.

What Happens

In a day's workshop I introduce participants to a glossary of information which will enable them to have an overview of my training program. My purpose is both to teach technique and to administer workouts. When the actual running of gaits and tempos becomes tiring it is time to write poetry, do stretching exercises and talk about running lore and related philosophy. The object is to shift between progressively more intense running and the factoring in of related new aspects. By the end of the workshop we will have learned all the gaits, experienced running after mediations and guided fantasy, loosened up with yoga and Feldenkrais exercises, written poetry, become introduced to action from personal center, and experimented with ways into our more subtle energies. Each person will also have a workout appropriate for their specific level of fitness, and suggestions for the continued uses of this method.

The Training Process

Variation in training is essential for people at all levels of fitness. I vary schedules for the beginner and for the experienced athlete in order to introduce as many physical and mental elements as possible. This means fartlek (speed play) intervals, varying gaits, breathing and resistance training. My main complaint with jogging is that it does not take into account the fact that people run differently depending on their body types and temperament as well as on their emotional cycles.

Man has been divided into three somatic types: endomorphic (obese), mesomorphic (muscular), and ectomorphic (slender). In my training I take into account these body types as well as the level of fitness.

Most coaches use both aerobic and anaerobic conditioning methods. To these two I add resistance training to build muscle and skeletal power. Resistance running puts the muscles under increased stress by means of running up hills, lifting weights, or doing power runs. Power runs create a natural muscle tension that builds strength.

The most difficult tool to use effectively is variation in tempo. Because each individual's oxygen and stamina level are different (and cannot be accurately measured) a lot of the running prescription I do is based on intuition and past experience. There are thousands of variations of oxygen debt workouts at my disposal. For instance, if we took six distances from 50 yards to one mile and combined these with six tempos and six rest periods we could come up with thousands of workout schedules. This variety allows for intensive workouts for competitors and very precise workouts for the novice.

As part of each workshop, I give detailed, individualized running programs and training schedules. They include instruction in breathing, gaits and tempos, musculoskeletal exercises, nutrition for health and performance, visualization and meditation techniques. It is the principles behind these tools, however, that help students evaluate their own progress. Each person moves differently and must be coached individually. Some glide easily but can't sprint well. Such persons should train mostly on good swing tempos and middle speed runs which are easy for them to "carry." Endomorphs may do better exercising in place: high knee lifts, power runs, or fresh swing tempos so the excess weight needn't be carried over the ground. A rather stiff mesomorph, such as I am, trains best on fast speeds and light running tempos. It is difficult for me to glide at my best speed for six miles. My body just does not gear in this fashion. An ectomorph friend of mine ran entirely middle-speed tempos. Another very thin friend ran successfully in races up to 50 miles without doing any speed work at all. His motion was so fluid that all he needed to do was tone his body and race every two weeks to keep razor sharp.

ometimes tempos can be put together into a repetition known s a "time trial." Time trials can be done at racing distance ut at perhaps various efforts, like 50 percent or 75 percent fort.

Developing someone's training program is much like uilding a house. If you don't prepare the foundation cor- ctly, it will fall down. If you don't proceed quickly, with a isionary eye to the future, you may move too slowly. For this ason even the novice has a goal, even if it is only running 20 yards at a gallop or a few minutes at a variety of faster mpos.

Physical conditioning improves in stages, by plateaus. he initial stage of twelve weeks should be divided into 65% ndurance, 25% speed or tempo and 10% resistance running, it each cycle afterwards should be a different ratio. These ter plans may be diverse for each person according to dividual goals and physical capacities.

The most basic principle is that we begin with the oadest base possible. This includes much running at shuffle d fresh swing tempos. The first twelve weeks is to build a undation. The object after the base has been laid is to arpen down progressively until the final peak for a year's aining is reached.

For each person I set some kind of physical goal. Whether is a time, distance, or mastery of a particular gait the setting specific goals is vital. An initial goal is to develop 'carry' d a sense of leg tempo while running at slight anaerobic etabolism. Initially the running gaits and tempos should be ne with long rest periods in between. Over a period of time e tempos of the runs will increase and the rests shorten.

The first twelve week cycle will be completed without any intensive anaerobic runs. The object from this period ward is to add sharpening workouts, anaerobic oxygen debt nning without draining the original twelve week base con- tioning. All set individual goals which can be anything from nishing a mile, seeing how far you can run in twelve minutes,

to utilizing a variety of gaits for a particular time period.

Each runner has a particular way of training. There are no absolute rules for each person, the role of the teacher or coach is to take the individual through the various stages and cycles. The coach must plan with and for the runner and often intuitively feel what should and can be done. But, he should not 'control' the runner. Percy Cerutty has said, ''If the athlete is not a free and full worker, working him to a fixed schedule, or according to the dictate of another person, such as a coach or authority, must end in confusion, disappointment, disillusionment, partial successes to what they might have been, breakdown, and eventual frustrations and abandonment.''

Progress that is sustaining is made by properly graduated schedules. Bill Bowerman of Oregon calls it the hard/easy method, Cerutty the Inclined Saw-Tooth Theory. ''Slowly and surely the organism must be subjected to steadily increasing loads. However, these loads cannot be added in continuous effort. There must be some cycle that we conform to, a period where the load is on, and a period when it is lightened. To subject the organism to a continuous and unremitting strain is to invite ultimate breakdown, even permanent injury.'' Therefore, the beginning runner trains three times a week, and the more advanced have an easy run every third day.

Besides the shifting of metabolisms, there is the necessity of running at a gait suitable to the speed or tempo at which you are moving. These shifting of 'gears' enables the body to flow through a run changing the leg action when suitable, and using the upper body to propel the torso. One technique, surging, is a means of bursting ahead of another runner in a race, or for training purposes to gain a sudden lift in energy and speed. Here is how it is done: while running at a fresh swing tempo, stretch the hands away from the sides at arm's length. Then cup the hands, pressing the thumb against the outside of the first finger between the knuckle and the front of the finger. As the thumb presses, somewhat like a stepping down on a gas pedal, make a ''bing'' sound in the larynx. On one sound the body will surge for approximately 10 yards either past an opponent, or if not in competition, merely for exhilaration.

In one run you may change the gait two or three times. A favorite of mine is to move from good swing to good speed to the canter. From the cyclical action of the swing tempo we begin shorting the steps and placing the foot plant just behind the toes. This allows one muscle group to rest while another is in action. From speed running I move into the canter. Presently I canter, thrusting with my left hand and pushing off with my right foot. The foot plant moves up to the toe, the arm moves outward and downward. The thrust is not done in a regulated pattern, but by a sense of the energy flow with which the runner becomes in touch. As the energy reaches the top, like the crest of a wave, the thrust and expelling forward is executed.

Form plays a large part, especially in the later stages of a hard run or race. The internal organism may be fatigued, but if the body can maintain proper momentum you will not falter. The practice of sprint form was taught to me by Lee Evans, world record holder at 400 meters, while we worked together at the Esalen Sports Center. The four-part process includes running with high knees, a full leg reach, visualizing your hands reaching out to shake hands and letting the air pull your elbow back, and running a foot above the head while making a chanting through your teeth you will be able to maintain poise though tiring in the last yards of a hard run.

As we learn more about body mechanics these and other techniques will become more important to the training process. Style of movement has been the most neglected aspect of athletic preparation.

For each runner there is a particular training. Trial and error will evoke that 'way' for yourself. A general trend is to move from easy aerobic running to progressively more difficult anaerobic running. As you enter peaking periods the organism will crave intense anaerobic runs, and become bored with less exciting training. To counteract this direction in order not to fizzle it is recommended that shuffling and fresh swing always remain at least 50 percent of the running. This balance will allow consistent improvement.

At the end of each cycle you should race or run hard frequently, while doing easy running on the days in between the efforts. This hard running will complete the cycle. Begin the new stage with a new balance of aerobic/anaerobic running. If it is late in the season you will do more intense anaerobic conditioning. In the fall or a new beginning cycle you should increase the aerobic conditioning. Eventually in the last peak of the season you may run short intervals in which the rest period can barely be distinguished from the actual run.

The thing to remember is that the process of training is a spiral. Each year, if you are consistent, you will see improvement. It is a matter of building layers of fitness on top of each other while sustaining what you have already developed. The end result is that the day will come when you are running faster and easier than you ever imagined. You will feel that your self has taken an unfair advantage. Enjoy, these God-like moments you have earned. At times surrender to the euphoria of success, and think about what the experience means in relation to the rest of your life.

Auxiliary Tools

There are a number of techniques which can be performed on a grass field or even inside your house. A helpful accessory is an ''executive jogger,'' a pad of sponge with springs inside that cushion the legs and knees against jarring during rapid movements. The executive jogger sells for less than $15 at sporting good stores. A run called ''short steps'' is a simple anaerobic technique which improves the quickness of leg action. Simply see how many steps you can take in a 15-yard space. Stamping and beating very quickly across a surface you will receive a light oxygen debt workout.

The Power Run

This is a technique of mine and a favorite. It involves dynamic (isometric) tension to create a resistance workout. It is done this way: throw one arm upward and step high with the opposite leg. Begin reaching for the sky with your hands while thrusting the leg high. The object of this exercise is not to travel down the field but to put the body in such a state of tension that regular gaits and tempos seem easy. This 'run' can only be done for a short period of time. It builds musculo-skeletal power throughout the body. After each power run it is advisable to stride out easily for a few yards. This run offers both resistance effort and an anaerobic exercise that contains elements of dynamic tension to promote upper body strength.

High Knee Lift

The high knee lift is a means of giving the heart and stomach muscles a workout when you cannot get out-of-doors. It can greatly aid city dwellers who have no grass to run on. Simply place hands on hips and lift the legs one at a time as high as possible towards the chest.

Running on the Spot

Running on the spot is a way to improve leg speed, and receive a light oxygen debt workout. If possible do this exercise on a grass field or with an executive jogger. Crouch over and fill the lungs with air. Stand erect and expel the air while making a sound in the larynx and run in place quickly as many times as you can before the body runs out of air.

Resistance Running

Find a sand hill of 30 yards or so. As you charge up the hill keep the arms at your sides and make a sound from the larynx. This run strengthens the legs, develops the chest and hardens the will! Sand allows you to abandon yourself to maximum effort because there is no fear of injury if you fall and it provides the kind of unresisting surface that requires extra effort.

Visualization

There is a natural stream of consciousness that results from running. The person who allows himself to acknowledge the flow of thoughts streaming through the mind while running will be pleasantly surprised. As a tool to enhance these states of awareness, I use a variety of guided images. The first I call ''The Big Hand.''

In this exercise visualize a big hand along the whole of your back giving assistance as you run at a shuffle or fresh swing. Lean into the hand when feeling fatigue.

Another visualization is the inner vision of a skyhook which holds you erect from the top of the hair. It holds you while it pulls you over the ground.

A third visualization I've used successfully is to imagine a wire being extended across a football goal post or spanning two trees. Visualize a harness across your chest and a wire connecting you to the wire that spans the two posts or trees. Let yourself be pulled toward the span by force, as if you are being reeled on a fishing line toward your goal.

Visualization techniques such as these will be among the most important aspects of athletic training in the future.

Breathing

As we are practicing our stride there is something else that requires attention. Breathing. Cerutty taught a method of releasing tension through the larynx. He believed one could make a conscious effort to exhale tension by expelling air in rhythmic patterns while running. In this *tidal breathing* you make a small sound from the epiglottis (from the throat not the abdomen) as you exhale. Each breath is different just as each wave of the ocean coming towards shore is different. As you expel the air you make a forward push to increase momentum. The idea is to enter a rhythm of breathing corresponding to your physical movement. If the breathing is asymetrical, that is, never in a routine or regular pattern, he thought, it was possible to make a physical breakthrough in running and experience a heightened state of awareness.

The breathing technique takes some time to master and it is more difficult to maintain as speed increases. You must begin slowly by taking air in without propelling forward, then releasing the air in unison while dropping the arms in front of you or at your sides and surging ahead. Breathing is sychronized with the arm movements but there is no fixed pattern. The action should be spontaneous.

During an intensive run you will spontaneously begin to change steps and alternate breathing patterns after you have mastered various gaits and tempos. Each person will develop a preference for certain gaits and sequences of tempos. Some people run on power, others on grace and flowing.

Rituals

I have experimented in my workshops with rituals before athletic activities. Using methods Esalen calls "energy work," I have two people stand with their palms together, right palm downward, left palm upward. At first, participants stand with palms only one-quarter inch apart. They begin to feel a sort of heat which is the creation of an energy field. After the field has been built up one participant frees himself and begins creating an energy field in his own hands by visualizing a small ball being formed between the hands. This force is then placed slightly below the partner's belly button and when the transfer is felt the runner begins down the field in fresh swing tempo and then breaks into the surge. Another ritual performed is to have two partners run toward an object, like a tree, and have one person send a telepathic message of what side of the the tree to run on. If the energy is "tight" between the partners, the message will be received.

Training Chart

The gaits and tempos described in the book provide both aerobic and anaerobic training effects as indicated below.* (Note: For the first three months 65 percent of one's training should be shuffle or fresh swing tempo for stamina development.)

These ratios are my own intuitive estimates.

	Endurance	Anaerobic
Shuffle	97%	3
Fresh swing tempo	85%	15%
TEMPO TRAINING		
Good swing tempo	75%	25%
Good speed tempo	75%	25%
Good speed to 8/10 EFFORT	65%	35%
Hard swing tempo	60%	40%
Surge	40%	60%
Arm swing action	50%	50%
Amble	90%	10%
Trot	75%	25%
Canter	55%	45%
Gallop	30%	70%
80 percent tempo or gallop	15%	85%
All out sprint	5%	95%
RESISTANCE RUNNING		
Power runs	30%	70%
Sand hills	15%	85%
AUXILIARY		
Short steps	40%	60%
Running on the spot	40%	60%
High knee lifts	80%	20%

*These are the approximate ratios of training effect for a person between the ages of 25-40 in reasonably good condition who is not seriously overweight.

Typical Workouts for
Endomorphic Women
Age 35-38

Day 1
Two minutes—shuffle
Three 50-yard shake-ups
25 high knee lifts
Two minutes—runs on spot
Two minutes—shuffle/walk
Two 60-yard—fresh swing
Two 60-yard—40-yard fresh/20-yard surge
Two 60-yard shakeups

Day 2
Swim for ten minutes

Day 3
Walk/shuffle for eight minutes
Three 50-yard shake-ups
Five 60-yard—fresh swing
Two 60-yard—40-yard fresh/20-yard surge

Day 4
Five minutes—shuffle
Three 20-second fresh swing, build only to 20 percent effort

Typical Workout for
Mesomorphic Women in Good Health
Age 30-33

Day 1
Five minutes—shuffle
Five 100-yard shake-ups
Four 80-yard—fresh swing tempo
Three 120-yard—90 yards at fresh swing/30 yards at swing
Four 110-yard—70 fresh swing/40 good speed
Three 100-yard—shake-ups

Day 2
18 minutes—shuffle/fresh swing
Four 100-yard shake-ups

Day 3
Ten minutes—shuffle
Four 100-yard shake-ups
Four 60-yards—sprint form, four-part sequence
Two 1-minute—fresh swing, build only to 40 percent

Typical Workout for Man Age 25-28
with Ecto/Mesomorphic Build

Day 1
Five minutes—shuffle
Four 100-yard shake-ups
Three 60-yard—sprint form
30 high knee lifts
Six 110-yard—canter
Four 120-yard—40 fresh/30 good speed/50 canter
Two 80-yard trot
Three 100-yard—80 fresh/20 surge
Two 80-yard shake-ups

Day 2
One hour—shuffle/fresh swing
Three 100-yard shake-ups

Day 3
5 minutes—shuffle
Four 100-yard shake-ups
Three 60-yard—sprint form
0 knee high lifts
Six 110-yard—go to canter
Three 80-yard—good speed
Two 80-yard shake-ups

Day 4
Ten minutes-shuffle
Three 1½-minute—fresh swing, build only to 40 percent
Two 150-yard—120-yard, good swing/30-yard, surge

Typical Workout for Ecto/Mesomorphic Man,
Master's Competitor, Age 45, with Best Mile of 5:10

Day 1
One-mile shuffle
Four 100-yard shake-ups
Four 60-yard—sprint form
Five 120-yard—fresh swing
Three 110-yard—good speed
Two 120-yard—90 fresh swing/30 surge
40 high knee lifts
Two 15-yard power runs
Four 100-yard shake-ups

Day 2
45 minutes—25 shuffle
15 minutes—fresh swing
2½ minutes—good swing
1½ minutes—sprint form
1 minute—arm swing action

Day 3
Two miles—fresh swing (40 percent effort)
Four 220-yard—up resistance hill (50 percent effort)
Two miles—good swing, build up to 70 percent effort
Six 120-yard—good swing, build up to 70 percent effort
Four 100-yard shake-ups

For Women

Much has been written in the last few years about the role of women in sports and athletics. In the area of distance running women have indicated a great proficiency in the marathon, and it has been surmised that the physical make-up of a woman's body is more adapted for endurance events that men. Joan Ullioyot, who is a world caliber marathoner and researcher in physiological changes in relation to running, has verified the endurance capability of women.

On a significant level we are all the same. The notion of a total person opening to their greater capacity holds similar promise for all people. The differences in possibilities for using running as a tool for self-discovery is minimal. Yet, there are some biological, sociological, and psychological differences between men and women which alter the ways in which they participate.

There is some evidence that women have a *greater* capacity for endurance events. A woman's percentage of body fat to overall weight is significantly more than a man's. Hypothetically, a woman's body is more suited for running a marathon, or swimming the English Channel. We will see tremendous improvements in competitive sports in this area in the near future.

I have spoken to many women who were outstanding runners in junior high school, many at 11 or 12 years of age were the fastest runners in their class. Many girls give up these activities and are steered into less ambitious pursuits because our culture is geared to socialize girls away from excellence in athletics. Many women can do yoga, dance, ski or a bit of tennis, but to sweat and push themselves to physical limits causes "perversions" in self-image and identity. I am surprised at the energy and desire to express themselves in physical terms which is ready to be released in many women.

In my experience I have found that women take to this training system easily. Much of the early adaption of the method has to do with details of setting up distances, and being aware of the means of movement. Also, the breaking up of the distances into segments allows for fluidity of body carriage. It seems that women have an easier time "flowing" into an activity than men who often will fully try to overpower an activity and end up bringing resistor muscles into operation which put brakes on natural energies.

A number of women have responded well to the training. One person, Marla Donnell, did especially well. She was a participant in a weekend workshop sponsored by the University of California, Davis. For four months I corresponded every two weeks with specific workouts for each day of running. Marla wrote enthusiastically that her physical condition was improving each day, and that the running was becoming easier and more enjoyable. She had marked out a grass field near her house and had measurered off various intervals. Later she visited a workshop I directed in San Francisco and the participants were impressed with her endurance and mastery of running techniques.

Women adapt easier to my running programs than most men. There are a number of reasons for this. First, the changes in gaits and tempos which I teach is similar to dance movements to which women have been accustomed. The activities which call for body awareness and attention to detail are suited to a woman's psychological make-up. Men are geared to improving times, to run faster over a given distance. The concepts of the integral training I recommend are designed to integrate grace, stamina, and speed. The running of short distances at particular gaits creates a pleasure-sense that is not a measurable outcome. Men's tendency toward immediate gratification and results cuts off many possibilities. I have found that women are more content to continue at the running training for the intrinsic benefits they are experiencing. Men often achieve the goal and lose the essence.

Power running in which the musculoskeletal system's strength is essential is more suited for the man's body and

psychology. The amble, trot and canter, as well as the tidal
breathing techniques are usually mastered by women. The
gaits which call for grace rather than speed or strength are
achieved more easily by women. I use the surge in my
teaching as a tool for women to learn to be more assertive.
Many women cannot make the sounds in the larynx helpful in
learning to surge forward. I often run at a fresh swing and
instruct a woman to follow me and surge past. Often this is
difficult for the woman to negotiate. When this happens I have
her repeat the process a number of times until the aggressive
instinct becomes expressed. The surge than becomes a means
for personal growth.

Igloi would have the women athletes almost stop training
during menstrual cycles. Women I have trained say this should
not be the case. Many women would like to have better locker
room facilities at town recreation areas and there is the
problem of getting into college and high school running
areas—and locked fences put everyone off.

Exercise, Stress and the Heart

If you haven't exercised regularly for a number of years, when
you begin there will be some soreness in your body. Most
people don't mind the regulatory aspects of this change, but
they do fear that their heart is not ready for the abrupt changes.
How can one be sure they are not putting themselves into
dangerous situations by embarking on an exercise program?
The truth is there is risk, and yet the promise of a healthy life
forces most to try some kind of exercise program. Yet there are
ways to determine capacity and suitability.

Those who come under my training, especially those with
a family history of heart disease, are urged to have tolerance
tests. The most common of these tests combine a treadmill or
bicycle with a standard electrocardiography machine that

measures the electrical signals of the heart's energy output. On the treadmill, for example, the speed of the walkway and the angle to the floor is increased in pre-set increments every few minutes, putting a stronger and stronger demand on the body for oxygen and therefore a stronger and stronger demand on the heart to pump more oxygen-rich blood to tissues.

Some people, though, have had experiences with "false positives." That means that while the tracings show the heart can't come up to its maximum potential for that patient under stress, X-rays of the coronary arteries show no damage or disease. Dr. David R. Redwood, chief of cardiovascular diagnosis at the National Heart and Lung Institute (NHL) in Bethesda, Maryland has said, "I'm afraid that these false positives will create cardiac cripples, people who are afraid to do anything, and for no reason."

An alternative to standard electrocardiograph is to have arteriography done. This is a test in which dye is injected into the heart and coronary arteries through a tube inserted through a major blood vessel in the arm. X-ray pictures are then taken to see if and where the coronaries are obstructed with fatty substances, a condition called *atherosclerosis*.

Instinctively I am able to tell fairly certainly whether a person is overexerting themselves during running. The surest signs are soreness and tiredness which will not decrease, and breathing that does not return to normal after a reasonable rest period. I test people at various levels of activity and observe their reactions. I do not tax someone at all until their muscle tone begins to improve noticeably. By this gradual input of training and teaching of techniques I have a good look at an individual before he embarks on taxing physical stress. Most research shows that people who have heart attacks while jogging, or having just taken up physical exercise would have been more likely to have had the problem if they had not begun to exercise.

CHAPTER IV

The Athlete of the Future

Will athletics in future generations be what they are now? I think not. I have my own personal vision of what the future of athletics will be. It includes an array of new methods, orientations, and approaches to sport and a new view of the mind and body. Athletics has always been a test of the total being, but in the future coaches, teachers and athletes will be keenly aware that the finest athletes and teams will be integrated people developing themselves in holistic ways. There will be a new sense that we bring our whole selves into the game.

Athletic people in the future will be concerned with coordinating physical and psychic experiences. In this context a new language will emerge which better describes various extraordinary occurrences. Athletic journalists will write in terms of a transpersonal vocabulary, as athletes will change from being reticent about explorations to an eagerness to participate in the latest training methods. Similar to the outer space language which emerged after Sputnik, concepts such as timelessness, precognition, and space/time laps will be accepted as valid ingredients of sport.

An athlete of the future, a runner for instance, will pay attention to style of perambulation as well as the speed and distances to be run. Disciplines such as rolfing and structural integration will help athletes realign the body so that it moves efficiently. Knowledge of the way the body moves will add awareness of self to the athletic act.

Eastern and Western philosophies will meet in a blending of disciplines, and the great athletes will be recognized as heroes of the spirit. In this context, athletics will demand larger utilization of the self. The auras and energy fields, the human biofield around our bodies will come into play. An athlete may perform rituals of centering and visualization before an activity. He will integrate all aspects of the self, intuition, sensing, thinking, and feeling into sport. In this framework, athletics will become a way to self-knowledge. Soon, after the taping for Saturday's football game is completed you may hear of hour-long sessions in which music, exercises, and suggestions are made to the team so that they emerge from the locker room with greater awareness.

There will be an attempt to modernize approaches and methods, but also a realization that the roots of athletics go deep, and that it is important to improve and reform. Natural rather than prefabricated principles will reappear—children will learn to walk differently, so they may be as quick as kittens, and gallop like horses or dogs. There will be reemphasis on relaxation. Methods such as Feldenkrais exercises, which break fixed patterns between mind and body, will enable us to sense the need for using specific muscles for particular movements. When movements are practiced in relaxed ways we will recognize resistors to fluid motion.

The mind and all the ramifications of innerspace will be incorporated in the body's achievements. The truth found in stillness will be transferred to the athletic act. Situations like Arthur Ashe meditating between sets at Wimbledon or Bruce Jenner, the world record holder in the decathalon, visualizing events and dreaming his plans will be integral to athletic preparation.

The athlete will train, in part, like a dancer, stretching each ligament and getting each joint to give its maximum flex. The athlete will strengthen the body with barbells and other devices. He will be particular about the muscles strengthened and know why and for what purposes. There will be a better understanding of anatomy, the ways and means of body movement. This will create a different sense of athletic action, not based entirely on split-second times and distances, but tuned into the bodily processes that allow heightened awareness. There will be new training methods which incorporate

musculoskeletal exercises, innerspace awareness, and more precise kinesthetic sensations. These new disciplines will make available extraordinary powers not before accessible through a training preparation. The places entered by these voyagers may seem dangerous, and there will be the understanding that true adventure often means the courage for free fall.

There should be no sanctity about the new way but simply the realization that athletics has been taught in an ice age, and that we seek a renaissance. The knowledge of previous individual teachers will be important, but the information will be so vast that it will be necessary to have coaching teams working together towards physical and spiritual fulfillment. It will not be uncommon for an athlete's day to include perhaps a session of polarity massage, an hour of guided fantasy meditation, a series of Feldenkrais exercises. In conjunction with training or during the off-season he may delve into structural integration, bioenergetics, join an ongoing interpersonal group or study aikido or tai chi chuan. Emphasis will be on preparation of the total person. Excellence in the particular sport or game will be a by-product.

Interscholastic, club and professional teams will lose their exclusively physical emphasis, and mesh with philosophy and the humanities. Physical education will be taught from the inside as well as the outside.

Nutrition will play an important part. We will learn not only what foods are best for health purposes, but what should be consumed in periods of extended activity, just before strenuous physical acts, or when the body needs recovery. It was discovered by the Russians that through a carbohydrate build-up in the few days prior to competition performance could be maximized. Pills and stimulants will cease to be crutches. The variance caused by these outside influences robs us of our personal resources.

Finally, and not so easily said, there will be a different feeling surrounding athletic events. They will remain serious but become joyful. Old concepts of superiority and dominance will subside. Individuals who have prepared for an event will see it as their day to experience something special together. The training build-up will be seen as a preparation rite for a voyage into the physical/spiritual world. And we will have some sense that our bodies belong to us but may be a part of a vast oneness, and that each rite we enter takes us closer to our larger potentials.

CHAPTER V

The Innerspaces of Running

The runner's mind is a drifting stream of consciousness often without formalized thought patterns. The oft-asked question, "why do you run?" is intimately tied to this. When the runner begins to explain his zest for running the explanation is without the essence discovered in the speechless act of the run.

During a run over a number of miles many thoughts pass through the mind. As an individual becomes more fit he spends less time concentrating on the physical activity and has the possibility of transcendence. With optimum fitness altered states of consciousness are possible. The state the mind enters when you are in excellent condition and running freely is similar in some ways to the mental set achieved in meditation.

Heightened awareness in running can be achieved by integrating meditation practices with physical activity. Running thoughts have a certain brilliance from the glow the body enters while running. But environmental distractions and physical fatigue take their toll upon awareness. The quietness achieved in meditation is more serene, but, something of its consciousness can be transferred to the body while running.

The goal is to close the gap between the states of awareness achieved while meditating and the reality of running.

Meditation is an ancient art. The states that spring from it have been given various classifications. For instance *bhavamukha* is an experience in which the mind borders between the absolute and the relative. *Bhava samadhi* on the other hand is an ecstasy in which the devotee retains his ego and enjoys communion with a Personal God. In *Nirvikalpa samadhi* all distinctions disappear, including the sense of a separate ego. I only mention these to show the possible diversity of human consciousness. Running awareness could have a similar diversity. Athletes at present do not have an adequate language to describe the richness of inner experience, nor have they traveled the paths necessary to bring it out fully.

Traditional mysticism regards the body as *maya*, an illusion from which we must find deliverance. A few seers, like Sri Aurobindo, believed the most transcendent powers of mind, what he termed, *Supermind,* could be brought down into the body. This modern Indian mystic believed an evolutionary transformation was possible on the plane of existence that occurs when the mind and body merge at their optimum capacities.

There are actual happenings which relate to these visions. The *lung gom* walkers of Tibet run hundreds of miles in trance state achieved mainly by meditation. Carlos Castaneda describes the Gait of Power the Yaqui indian Don Juan could perform to enable him to sprint in the forest at night. Who knows what states of awareness are reached in a 3:52 mile or marathon run at under a 5:00 mile pace?

What we forget in the haste of the run is that the inner world can be our deliverance. Sometimes a deep joy comes after a long beautiful run which is completed by going inside to affirm the satisfaction. An important realization for me has been that my inner being does not necessarily have to relate to my physical body. Each day can produce a different spiritual ity as well as physical presence. It has taken me a long time to realize this.

One day in Eugene, Oregon, the United States running capitol, I came upon new meaning. My legs were heavy with pained tendons. My run ended in a walk and I sat under a tree and closed my eyes and went inside. I was like a block, legs folded under me like a concrete slab. That night I dreamed I was running in a familiar place surrounded by fine books and an old favorite coach as my private tutor—but the scene was in a prison. This may have something to do with the experience of being trapped inside my physical body when an injury overwhelms all other existence. Could it be that if I could go inside to a deeper core of my being that overall being-awareness would set in? Is it that the burned out athlete can't manipulate his physical being because he is not aware of internal processes.

The inner world constitutes deliverance for the athlete as well as the person seeking maximum health. By slowing down thoughts the inner journey allows balance, poise, self-understanding; inner world awareness can mean completeness. Physical improvement is only one criteria of personal growth and well-being. Mental awareness and spirtual disciplines are s important in creating a snythesis as are the runner's times.

Expanding the use of exercises to include the mental aspects calls for visualization techniques that enable the natural running consciousness to grow richer. These mental techniques could be as basic to conditioning as physical activities. Beginning practice could begin with five minutes of contemplation in the morning and evening. Allowing yourself to sit or lie down in a quiet place, close your eyes, and allow the thoughts that present themselves to flow through your mind. Be the witness rather than the possesor of the thoughts, and become aware of the unfolding of your innerspace.

Disciplined running is a kind of meditation in itself, without the addition of any specific mental exercise. But by

paying attention to the mental side of it you can deepen an
enlarge the experience. Here are some meditation exercises.

Sit in a place near your running course, eyes shut (or ope
just enough to focus softly on the ground in front of you), an
simply count your breaths. Don't force your breathing, just le
it happen, and when you have counted ten exhalations star
again and count to ten once more. Do this for fifteen or twent
minutes. If your mind wanders and you miss a breath, star
again. Don't be discouraged if your mind wanders; simply sta
with the exercise and see what develops.

Now start walking, holding the same kind of focuse
awareness. Focus on the feeling at the soles of your feet, o
upon the ground directly in front of you. After a minute or tw
begin to run at a shuffle or fresh swing, keeping your attentio
on your feet or the ground. If thoughts intrude, return to th
first place of focus.

You can experiment with other ways to place your aware
ness, for example on the feel of your gait or tempo, or on
point of tension in your body, or upon the stream of con
sciousness itself. The main thing is to take the spirit o
meditation directly into your running. Each mental exercis
tends to have certain consequences however; this you wi
learn from practice. By focusing on your points of tension, fo
example, you might uncover emotions connected to them o
find other points of imbalance.

I have been exploring the inner life for a year and a hal
I've begun to close the gap between the awareness I sens
while meditating and my consciousness in running. One afte
noon at meditation I sat for a few minutes and allowed m
thoughts to travel through my mind knowing I would run lat
with a state of greater awareness. I thought I heard an Italia
song being played in a city tenement. This image was followe
by images of the Etruscans, an ancient tribe of Italy. Ther
were also smells of my grandfather's house, and assorte
memories of my youth. I began running with Mike Murph

around the Marina Green. At various junctures Mike instructed me to drop the thoughts that would enter my mind. We ran many laps, increasing the tempo with each successive lap. As our minds became ''clearer'' we ran harder with fuller abandonment. Running harder and harder until our bodies gave out. Afterwards we felt ''floaty'' and experienced the sensation as if we had stared too long into the sun. The concentration had become so intense that it seemed we had run past our physical endurance. The experience was a lesson in the powers of mental awareness.

A practice we do in workshops is to sit randomly in a grass field and quiet our thoughts. We do this for a few minutes until we are ready to run. We then stand and, keeping our eyes half-closed, run first at swing tempo followed by a surge. We then return to the meditation position a number of times to clear thoughts, and than rise again and run. In this way we practice bringing the meditation awareness closer to running consciousness.

In joining the reflective discipline of meditation with running I find that the philosophy of Sri Ramana Marharshi possesses the depth and simplicity to enable a mind/body integration. Marharshi, a modern Indian, prescribed a basic means to unfoldment of the self. He felt the direct path to knowledge was the inquiry, ''Who am I?'' It is a means to transcend the physical. ''If I am not the five cognitive sense organs, viz. the sense of hearing, touch, sight, taste, and smell, which apprehend their respective objects, viz. sound, touch, color, taste and odor, I am not; the five cognitive organs, viz. the organs of speech, locomotion, grasping, excretion, and procreating, which have as their respective functions, speaking, moving, grasping, excreting, and employing, I am not; the five vital airs, prana, etc., which perform respectively the five functions of in-breathing, etc. I am not; even the mind which thinks, I am not; the nescience too, which is endowed only with the residual impressions of objects, and in which there are no objects and no functioning, I am not.'' From the basic "dropping" of thoughts I have passed to an intense and profound meditation. It can be done between runs or in the evening after a run or to begin the day. When people seeking healthful joy from physical activities add the inner dimension a new brand of physical education, athletics and sport will emerge.

Ways to Altered States of Consciousness with Running

Running, with its various gaits, tempos, and breathing patterns, joined with disciplines for heightened awareness can be a way of discovering our larger selves. I am finding that average people as well as superstars touch spritual elements when they least expect it—running down a road at dusk, or even around a monotonous track. Sometimes a happy day is enhanced by an enjoyable run. Other times depression, tiredness, a lonely ennui can be transformed into euphoria through running. At present I am not sure why these sensations occur, nor is there a language to explain their appearance. But, we are discovering ways and paths by which these occurrences may happen with greater regularity.

Breathing and awareness of breathing can be a voluntary or involuntary function—it can be subtle or an all consuming experience. Breathing is the controlling factor in the run, but large numbers of people are not aware of their breathing cycles. When breathing is restricted it is impossible to run with a relaxed fluid movement. Restricted breathing causes the shoulders to sway while the individual gasps, rather than taking in air with long steady intakes. Percy Cerutty taught movements in which the breathing is syncronized with the running movements. He termed these synchronizations the trot, canter, and gallop. When you attempt to learn these movements at thirty years of age they are difficult to master.

Presently I am beginning to infuse these gaits into my most intensive runs. When I am able to do it successfully, I find that control of breathing is the principle factor in maintaining my style.

Deep breathing when done after running allows connection with the subtler energies of the body. Even on days when the run itself was tedious you can gain pleasure by reclined awareness following the run. To add to your pleasure and relaxation visualize air entering through the lungs and being released on exhalation through the toes and fingertips.

Meditation-stilling the mind to turn running into a form of self-discovery. Participants in *zazen*, a form of sitting meditation, are known for spending hours watching thoughts pass through their minds. At times during this experience there is a space in which the meditator senses a timeless consciousness. When this consciousness is combined with the awareness of running amazing things happen.

Recent scientific discoveries show that the most inhibiting factor in muscular activity is the production of lactic acid in the blood. Lactic acid escapes from the muscles to the bloodstream when the supply of oxygen is inadequate. Breakthroughs in sport will be achieved when we learn how to reduce lactic acid. *Scientific American* has published medical reports indicating that ten minutes of meditation can reduce lactic acid in the blood as much as eight hours of sleep does. At the Esalen Sports Center we have added meditation to our running program between sets of runs and after each workout.

I am experimenting with various sequences to blend meditation consciousness with running. Once, at a workshop entitled ''Trail Running and the Archetypes of Sport,'' I had a group of randomly chosen people participate in a 5-mile run through the Mount Tamalpais countryside north of San Francisco as the completion of a sequence.

We begin by sitting in a circle and pronouncing the sound

OM. During the trail running workshop we found a cave, and group cohesion was aided by the echoing resonance found there. We made the *OM* sound together 36 times. In unison we became a chorus of sounds and breathing intakes. These sounds were followed by quiet meditation in which the object of concentration is the natural thoughts which pass through the mind. This aspect of mind, the witness self, allows a person access to their own thinking processes. When thoughts linger follow them rather than fight them away. At times it helps to visualize an entrance and exit. Allow your thoughts to go through the entrance and pass towards the exit. Other times close the exit and let the thoughts store up. Open the exit and let the thoughts flush out.

We then began walking in a small circle first getting in touch with grace and balance by touching heel to toe with each swing of the leg. After the circle was completed, we gathered the group into a pack and began shuffling together while visualizing ourselves as a primordial band. I set the pace while a helper took up the rear as shepherd. There should be a minimum of talk, trying to maintain the state of consciousness attained in the meditation. Sometimes the group sounds like a herd of horses, and physical fitness and group solidarity are gained together. This sequence can be repeated a number of times throughout the day or weekend.

Guided fantasy work enables a person to become more aware of their internal processes and begin to visualize themselves as they would like to be. A good way of helping people to visualize themselves is to bring them into a deep state of relaxation and suggest positive images. A favorite of mine focuses on basic relaxation. I begin by asking people to get in touch with their breathing. This can be done by placing one hand on the abdomen and breathing into the other hand. From this voluntary breathing, close your eyes and visualize a white light like a halo over your head. Take a breath in and draw the white light down into your body as far as your eyes. Next visualize walking out onto a beautiful grass field. On this field is a large rock. Climb on top of the rock and relax, feeling serene and calm. Picture yourself sitting on top of this rock in the bright, warm, sunlight. For a moment enjoy the sun on your body while breathing the light from the halo down through your chest, abdomen and pelvis area into your knees, ankles and feet. Now think of your body as a rubber stamp and the floor as an ink pad and allow yourself to sink into the floor. If you feel tension in a particular area of your body, or if you have a real or imagined injury in one area of your body, draw the light from the halo over your head to the spot of tension or injury. Don't demand that your body heal itself, give it space to find its own health. Simply relax in the sun and breathe light into various areas of your body.

Flexibility and suppleness is important I have a tendency to neglect flexibility exercises, and presently work with two yoga teachers in trying to catch up. When I was a youngster I disliked doing exercises. I was embarassed that I could not touch my toes or do forward rolls. It has taken me a long time to realize that flexibility systems not only allow injury-free fluid motion, but effect the mind in a calming way that balances out some of the more intensive running experiences. I am distrubed at some yoga books which describe comple

poses but fail to give the basics. The 40-minutes of yoga I presently do has brought a loss of pain and soreness in my body. I never touch my toes or bend into pretzel like contortions, but I am more aware of my spine, my balance, my capacities. The development of flexibility and suppleness is extremely important. However, everyone must decide for themselves how much is beneficial and how much is disruptive to enlightened awareness.

An interesting flexibility system was developed by Moshe Feldenkrais, a former physicist and judo master. He found his own solution to a knee injury by experimentation with the various ranges of movement in his knee joint. This led to the development of a system of movements which break the fixed patterns we generally operate with during mind/body interactions.

There are thousands of Feldenkrais exercises (if you are interested, I recommend you read this book, *Awareness Through Movement*), but the one I find which best exemplifies the methods is used to create a greater range of flexibility in arm rotation. Extend your right arm horizontally from the shoulder, swing it back to the right as far as comfortably possible. Mark the spot indicating the range of flexibility on the wall. Now swing your arm back again as far back to the right as you comfortably can, but move your head to the left. Repeat this motion five times (head to the left and arms to the right). Now add to this movement letting your eyes follow your arm to the right, and do this movement five times (arm to the right, head to the left, and eyes to the right). After allowing your body to do these patterns to which they are unaccustomed, when you raise your right arm and bring it back comfortably you will have about a 20 percent improvement in your range of flexibility. Interestingly, if you raise your left arm and bring that back as comfortably as you can and mark the spot on the wall, the same range of improvement can be gained by doing the above patterns in your mind while your eyes are closed.

The Chinese teach that the center of our being is located directly below the bellybutton. It is supposed that if our movement originates from the area directly below the navel area, rather than directly behind the eyes as do most Westerners, a free and balanced sensation will accompany our movements. Recently at a conference with the International Track Association in Eugene, Oregon, particular attention was paid to the running style of Ben Jipcho, the prolific Kenyan who has won almost every professional distance race. He seemed to move more from his pelvic area than around the shoulders. His motion seemed more of a glide than a pull. A body that moves from center is in harmony with itself; focus and concentrated effort minimize stress.

An exercise I find useful in learning to move from center begins by walking slowly with special awareness to a spot inches below your bellybutton, the *haru chakara* point. Look off into the distance and walk from that point into a non-defined distance. After some practice a partner is chosen, and that person places a hand on your upper chest while you walk focused on your centering area. The partner randomly applies resistance by placing a hand on your upper chest. As you gain center your movement forward cannot be dictated by another's resistance. Balanced, your energy allows you to move through barriers without effort.

Balancing of energy is also possible through acupuncture. For two years I suffered with pains in my satorius muscle which runs from the hip to the inner side of the shinbone, crossing the thigh obliquely in front. I often felt a numbness in my limbs that made it difficult for me to stand up without favoring one side of my body. The sensation would come and go, making sustained training difficult.

I made the acquaintance of Dr. William Brostoff, a San Francisco physician who specializes in internal medicine, psychosomatic medicine, and acupuncture. On my third visit I had the experience of the needles being put in just the correct pattern around the spot of soreness in my knees. There was a whirling energy happening inside my leg, a speeding up of the healing process as if all the bodies energies were directed to one location. In the next days my knee felt much better. It was a great relief as I had been Feldenkraised, osteopathed, rolfed, chiropracticed, and had lifts in my shoes. All the external manipulations didn't help as much as a basic shift in my own personally generated energy. Ocassionally the tendon trouble returns. I am now aware it is often accompanied by stress, unintelligent overuse, or personal anxiety. I don't panic as much over its reappearance. I have been able to become the observor, watch it, not be defeated by it, and learn from the message it is sending my way. *Transcending the physical body into the self outside the flesh: the auras, prana fields and subtle energies of our being.* This is a method developed by George Leonard, author the *The Ultimate Athlete,* and is derived from his aikido training with Robert Nadeau. In the practice of aikido much time is spent finding and utilizing *ki* energy, powers that are outside our physical selves. The presence of this human biofield, and its application to movement and athletics could foster other more far-reaching experiments and reforms.

By placing your hands, one palm up and the other palm down, over a partner's allowing an inch of space between you hands, if you move your hands in a circular motion you will begin to feel a sensation: heat, electric current, stinging. Beginning from this connection, transference of energy from one person to the next is possible. I have had runners lay their hands on the small of another's back and transmit generated energy that carries through to a run. What the further use of this transference could mean for the preparations of important athletic activities is both exciting and speculative. *Interpersonal understandings in relation to athletics, sports and games*. Bob Kriegel, cofounder and former director of the Esalen Sports Center has established a two year project with the focus on developing self-awareness through Sports and Games (SAGAS). I am one of 16 members in the project which meets one week each summer, and one weekend and one evening each month. Much of the early work in the project has centered on interpersonal processing. Having little experience in group process, I was amazed at the issues that could arise from the interplay of volleyball games, wrestling and centering exercises, and new types of games.

I ran in a two-mile race in the evening the last day of the week's summer session. Going into the race I was feeling depressed. Although I had not been an active verbal participant I felt drained by the experience. Half way into the race the depression turned into euphoria. The week had performed a cleansing, a unique beauty-sense overcame me as I ran my fastest two-mile in five years.

Friends mentioned how relaxed my form looked during the race. I had tried for years to stop pulling my shoulders up to my ears at the crucial points of races. I had tried visualizing weights on my elbows, flapping my front wing muscles up and down. During this race I could sense my shoulder's drop and air move rhythmically into my lungs. It was not technique that lowered shoulders but a new sense of worth and essence.

The importance of exercise in relation to personal well-being: physical improvement programs as part of therapeutic services. Most neighborhood saunas and gymnasiums do not allow men, women, and children to exercise together, but "fun runs" and recreational sports give the promise of participation at all levels of ability. With access to these services by local clubs and agencies there is a great opportunity for professional counselors to incorporate the physical and the therapeutic.

One aspect of my work as a physical fitness counselor is the development of running programs for an entire family. Arthur Deikman, a San Francisco psychiatrist, was enthused by Michael Murphy's involvement with running and at 45 took up the activity. I began meeting him for workouts and eventually his wife, Etta, and daughters, Susie and Cathy, became interested. Presently I instruct each one privately and as a group and a family enthusiasm has developed. Etta recently was able to square dance far into the night for the first time in 15 years. Susie has progressed to the point of being able to join the high school cross-country team if she feels so inclined, Cathy is now able to perform modern dance without tiring. Arthur will soon be one of the better 880 runners in the over-45 category in northern California. *Age is not a deterrent*. Jack La Lanne, for his 60th birthday recently, swam, with his hands and legs bound and pulling a 1,000 pound boat, from Alcatraz Island to Fisherman's wharf, a distance of about one mile. His goal was to improve his time of a few years before. Percy Cerutty was anxious to return to Australia when he lived with me in the summer of 1974. With all the clinics and speaking engagements he had gotten a bit out of physical shape. He wanted to go back to Portsea, Australia, and see how fast he could run the mile. He was 80. Richard Marsh is a 62-year-old professor of creative arts at San Francisco State. Over the last 8 months I have added running schedules to his regime of yoga and weight training. This year in the annual walk/run along the famous 7.8-mile Bay-to-Breaker (San Francisco Bay to the Pacific Ocean) trail he improved over his previous year's performance. Michael Murphy ran faster for the mile when he was 44 than when he was 43, and faster when he was 45 than he did at 44.

These examples and hundreds like them seem to prove it is never too late to increase, begin to improve, or restore your physical capacities.

What I have attempted in this chapter is to give a broad overview of some of the disciplines which, when blended into the running experience, may enable you to use them as self-discovery. There is no predicting when an altered state-of-consciousness experience may happen. Some appear after sustained diligence, other's occur quite by chance: The lady skydiver who saw angels when sailing in an updraft may never experience them again; could David Meggyesy again foresee the plays in advance as he did after being hit on the head during a professional football game? My most profound running experience happened 9 years ago during a six-mile run in the countryside outside Syracuse, New York. Does my present involvement in mind/body disciplines assure a similar experience? I don't think so. On the other hand, Uyeshiba, the founder of aikido could place his body in two locations at one time, biolocation. A film strip, which admirers swear was not tampered with, shows him move many yards in a fraction of a second. Percy Cerutty could place an athlete in a trance before world record attempts. These ''powers'' came from a life devoted to a particular use of self-knowledge.

Everytime I turn someone on to running I almost hope they learn to limit their goals because if they don't, if running becomes a part of them, there is no turning back and the philosophy of life I have built around running begins to apply to them also. There will still be many pleasant moments, but there will always be the striving to achieve the supreme moment and the knowledge that they don't happen often.

I have a friend who has gone over the line. I can see myself talking to him, saying all the words so that I know for certain he will be ready when that supreme moment of success will come. I visualize the moment at the start when he will run a 5:00 minute mile, and because of the many hours of thought I've put in it, I get jealous when he thinks of something else. So we wait for the moments of illumination. How can we do otherwise? That ecstasy far removed from the blisters, the hot

sun, shortness of breath, can't save you from the many miles in front of you. You are trapped in an earthly body which knows few ways out into deliverance-enlightenment. It is such an ecstasy as you go deeper, and it all feels so natural. The world is only to be observed and you are the observer who doesn't even have to judge, but all the lofty ideals in the world can't save you from the ordeal in front of you. But the moments, the magic ones, get you through because we all believe in the myths of ourselves, all the stories we told ourselves years ago. Maybe you can find one moment where the sun is beginning to set, where the fog rolls in, and maybe you are running with just that person who gives you the right feeling, and the ground is smooth and fast. You have known the tension and now the freedom. There is only you and your companion and it is almost absurd how important you make it all. But why not important? What else?

SPORT AS YOGA
Altered States of Consciousness
&
Extraordinary Powers*

Michael Murphy

For the past two years, I have collected stories about the connections between sport, philosophy and religion. This project grew out of responses to *Golf in the Kingdom,* a novel in which I described a mind-opening game of golf and day-long sojourn with Shivas Irons, a philosopher-athlete I met by chance in Scotland during the summer of 1956. When I wrote the book I hadn't realized there were so many others who had fallen through similar star-gates. For relatively few sportspeople have the language or philosophy to interpret altered states like these, and very little of it finds its way into their biographies or into their reports to the media.

The material I am gathering has led me to construct the frameworks that appear below. Because these reports of transcendence are similar in so many ways to those of shamans, Sufis, Zen masters and yogis, I am led to believe that for some people sport is a liberating discipline of sorts, a kind of yoga or *sadhana* in the making. There are many differences, of course, between ordinary athletics and the classical contemplative in disciplines. I am only suggesting that there are surprising and significant similarities.

*This essay originally appeared in *News from Esalen*

A. Altered states of consciousness in sport.

The list of categories below could be extended inde finitely, for the varieties of mystical experiences are endless; i will certainly be changed as we gather more stories. Ever experience included in it has some or all of the aspect described by the other categories: for example, there wa intense enjoyment or ecstasy in almost every instance.

1. *Extraordinary clarity, as if the doors of perceptio were suddenly opened.* John Brodie, the San Francisco 49e quarterback, described this state in the December 1972 issue o *Intellectual Digest:* "Often, in the heat and excitement of game, a player's perception and coordination will improv dramatically. At times, and with increasing frequency now, experience a kind of clarity that I've never seen adequatel described in a football story. Sometimes, for example, tim seems to slow way down, in an uncanny way, as if everyon were moving in slow motion. It's beautiful."

Tony Jacklin, Britain's famous professional golfer, de scribed a similar state in the November 4, 1973 issue of th *Sunday Times of London:* "It's not like playing golf in a drean or anything like that. Quite the opposite. When I'm in thi state everything is pure, vividly clear . . . I'm living *fully* i the present, not moving out of it. [This state] comes and goes and the pure fact that you go out on the first tee of tournament and say 'I must concentrate today,' is no good. won't work. It has to already be there."

The statement that such a state must "already be there, that it can't be commanded by simple admonitions or brut will, is characteristic of the yogic and mystical literature. Suc states come like visitations, like grace. In the same *Time* article Jacklin says that he has experienced them about te times in his life.

2. *Extraordinary focus and concentration.* Quoting Jacklin again: "When I'm in this state . . . I'm in a cocoon of concentration. And . . . I'm invincible . . . I'm absolutely engaged, involved in what I'm doing at that particular moment." He described such a moment during the Trophee Lancome tournament outside Paris in 1970, when he reached "the purest psychological state" in his life. On the next to last hole of the tournament, "everything came into focus. Although I could feel my club at every half-inch of my swing, I was free from thinking about various parts of my game. I hit my drive 350 yards, about 50 yards further than I had ever hit a ball in my life." In this state he eagled the hole, birdied the next and won the tournament by one stroke ahead of Arnold Palmer.

3. *Emptiness. A sense of nothingness or void.* Much contemplative philosophy is built upon the experience of emptiness, in which the perceiving ego gives way to the void. Something like this state has been described by ocean divers and professional football players. Once while I was playing golf, there was a stupendous silence in which the other players, the golf course, the distant hills seemed suspended in air. Although some sense of effort remained, my actions seemed to happen by themselves.

4. *Deautomatization.* A breaking of the perpetual constancies. For example, the flow of time may alter. Racing driver Jackie Stewart has described the uncanny sense of things slowing down in a race, permitting him to make maneuvers that would be impossible in his ordinary state.

Or people may begin to look different. David Megzyesey, the St. Louis Cardinals' linebacker, described a game in which he saw auras around the other players. He could anticipate the moves his opponents were about to make in kind of precognitive playing trance.

With old habits suspended, new powers have a chance come into play.

5. *Equality. A perception of oneness everywhere.* Such feeling may come with greater or lesser degrees of intensi and may last for a second or for days. A mountain climber know was in this state for a week after a climb in Nepal, spite of the fact that he lost some of his toes to frostbit During his a descent from the mountain, he was "enveloped a psychic fire that came with a vision of (his) future life. Afterwards he felt an all-encompassing unity. Everywhere, everything, one presence held the world.

6. *Access to larger energies, insights and behavior.* Sometimes one seems to be lifted into other realms, wher power, beauty and invincibility are the natural state of things In this state, a new and larger self comes into being.

Mike Spino, a former college distance champion and no director of a research project in sport at Esalen Institute described such an experience. In the winter of 1967, he wa training on a dirt and asphalt, paced by a friend who wa driving a car. He had intended to run six miles at top speec but after the first mile he was astonished at how easily he coul do it. He had run the first mile in four and a half minutes wit little sense of pain or exertion. It was as if "he was carried by huge momentum." The wet pavement and honking horns wer no obstacle at all. Then his body had no weight or resistance. "began to feel like a skeleton as if the flesh had been blown of the bones." He felt like the wind. Daydreams and fantasie disappeared. The only negative feeling was a guilt for bein able to do this.

When the run was over, he couldn't talk, for "he didn know who he was." Was he "the one who had been runnin or was he Mike Spino?" He sat down by the road and wept. He had run the entire six miles on a muddy roadside at a four-and-a-half minute pace, which was close to the national record, but now there was "a crisis deciding who he was."

7. *Communication with or perception of disembodied entities.* A lady skydiver who had read *Golf in the Kingdom* told me that the book reminded her of a time when she road a thermal up-wind on her parachute for over an hour while a company of dazzling figures danced around her—figures with human shapes made of nothing more substantial than light. She was a mother and sensible housewife, a practical earth-bound type, she said, but that experience had made her believe in something like angels. Her vision could be dismissed as an hallucination, but that would not explain its convincing quality or its power and beauty. She had never had an experience like it, and the glowing figures seemed utterly real.

Her vision resembles the spirit visitations so often described by people at sea. Joshua Slocum, the first man to sail along around the world, in his classic tale of that historic voyage, tells about the appearance of a "helpful sailor" who talked to him for hours in Portugese. This disembodied figure claimed to have been the pilot of the Pinta during the voyage of Columbus, and shared some of his knowledge with Slocum. These are many accounts of such "helpful sailors." Being at sea may induce a state of mind like that produced through deliberate sensory deprivation. In such a state, normal perceptions may break down to open the way for other kinds of seeing-whether of projections from the person's own mind or of beings with a life of their own.

8. *Ecstasy, delight, supreme aesthetic enjoyment.* In Sanskirt there is the word *ananda* to denote the delight of existance without which the world would collapse. The pleasures, joys, and ecstasies that occur in sport are at the heart of

playing, they are the ultimate reinforcer. Every athlete
—professional or amateur, proficient or not-so-proficient
—whom I have questioned has said that enjoyment is the real
name of the game.

In his book *First Four Minutes,*, Roger Bannister tells
about a day in Scotland: "Soon I was running across the moor
to a distant part of the coast of Kintyre. It was near evening
and fiery sun clouds were chasing over to Arran. It began to
rain, and the sun shining brightly behind me cast a rainbow
ahead, It gave me the feeling that I was cradled in the rainbow
arc as I ran.

I felt I was running back to all the primitive joy that my
season had destroyed. At the coast the rainbow was lost in the
particles of spray, beaten up by the breakers as they crashed
against the granite rocks. . . . The gulls were crying overhead
and a herd of wild goats were silhouetted against the headland.
I started to run again with the sun in my eyes nearly blinding
me. I could barely distinguish slippery rock from heathery tuft
or bog, yet my feet did not slip or grow weary now—they had
new life and confidence. I ran in a frenzy of speed, drawn on
by an unseen force. The sun sank, setting the forest ablaze,
and turning the sky to dull smoke. Then tiredness came on and
my bleeding feet tripped me. I rolled down a heather topped
bank and lay there happily exhausted."

B. Extraordinary powers, or *Siddhi* in Sport

Siddhi is the Sanskrit word for those extraordinary powers
or capacities which emerge with the practice of a liberating
discipline. The aspirant is often warned against the glamour a
particular *Siddhi* has for him, for it may produce an enchant-
ment that leads him away from the liberation he seeks. *Moksha*
before *Siddhi*—liberation before powers—is a constant adage

in the contemplative literature. However, even in the strictest traditional systems the pursuance of a *siddhi* may be permitted if it seems important to the aspirant's growth. But because this occult world is a complex and often perilous realm, the explorer usually needs guidance through it. If sport were to open up to these kinds of things, it would probably have to draw upon the ancient wisdom as it developed its own guides and maps. NOTE: (The physical power, or *siddhi* is listed first, followed by the psychological or spiritual change that goes with it and then by an example from the world of sport. The list of *siddhis* is drawn from the various religions and shamanistic traditions.)

PHYSICAL SIDDHI	PSYCHIC ANALOGUE
1. Extraordinary control of the bodily processes.	Control of feelings, thoughts, imagination and other psychic processes.

1a. Mastery of pain, both psychic and physical

1b. Ability to survive with little or no oxygen, e.g. when a yogi is buried alive.

1c. The Tibetan *tumo;* the ability to generate heat from within the body with little or no muscular exertion.

| 2. Ability to change shape, size and mass. | Psychic mobility, altered consciousness. |

FROM SPORT

This is fundamental to all high level performance in sport. Pulse, heart beat, breathing and other physiological processes come under extraordinary control when a runner does the marathon in a little over two hours (which means that he averages better than a mile every five minutes for the entire 26 miles) or when underwater swimmers hold their breath for more than five minutes at depths of up to forty feet, or when a race driver makes the hairpin turns required in Grand Prix driving.

The transcendence of pain in football, boxing, wrestling and other sports borders on the miraculous. Football players have gone through games with broken ribs, noses, toes and fingers. Boxers have finished fights with broken hands and wrists. Often there was no pain at all during the contest, so great was the player's concentration.

The anaerobic abilities of ocean divers and distance runners.

Mountain climbers and ocean swimmers report similar abilities to withstand freezing temperatures.

Morehei Uyeshiba, the inventor of Aikido, it is said, seemed to change his shape and size in the swirl of a free-form match. Drastic changes in body image have been reported to me by golfers, football players, ocean divers, skydivers and mountain climbers; sometimes such a change seems to communicate itself to onlookers.

3. Invisibility	Ego-loss, blending, harmonizing with the elements.
4. Auras, lights, the odor of sanctity, emanations of energy.	Acting as a channel for higher levels, "manifesting the Divine."
5. Levitation.	Sustenance by other energies, by the "ki" or *prana* of the Eastern disciplines.
6. Bilocation, being in two places at once.	Astral travel, power to impress at a distance.
7. Stigmata, tokens of espousal and other signs on the body.	Conforming to a religious or philosophical ideal or to a "Higher Form," singleness of being and purpose.
8. Ability to pass through solids.	Inner emptiness, loosening of ordinary psychic structures.
9. Incombustability and impassability.	Inner equality, imperturbability, identification with the ultimate being and delight.
10. Incorruptability at death, and freedom from the aging process.	Contact with the ever-born, ever-renewed, self-existent being which is characteristic of higher states.

The same Master Uyeshiba, in a movie of him demonstrating Aikido, seems to disappear from view for an instant then reappear in another place. His followers swear the film was never tampered with. There are legends about similar feats among football players. George Best, the Irish soccer star, has been described as "going underground" or "going invisible" during a match. (See David Ponsonby's article "Soccer in the Kingdom" in *Soccer America*, May 29, June 5, 1973).

Again in Aikido, where the perception of "ki" is part of the discipline, many participants claim that they have seen an energy field around themselves or others. (See for example George Leonard's article in the June, 1973 issue of *Intellectual Digest* or Koichi Tohei's book entitled *Aikido in Daily Life.*) What was that lady skydiver seeing when she saw those "forms of light" tumbling down the wind around her?

A form of levitation appears in some of the martial arts when the participant is taught to make himself lighter or heavier at will through the manipulation of "ki".

David Smith, in his unique pentathalon, described the sensation of "rising above his body" while he was swimming. The "out of the body experience" is frequently reported by athletes.

Could it be argued that the sometimes radical changes of body structure which an athlete goes through in order to perform a particular feat or to play a particular position is like this? The same power of mind over matter is involved.

Again, in Aikido (and Kung Fu), there is something called "mesh practice" in which the participant imagines—then becomes—a net through which an opponent's energy and body may pass. I have never heard of someone actually passing through a solid object, but the practice goes in that direction. In karate, the power to split boards and bricks is ascribed as much to "ki" as it is to sheer muscular force.

In firewalking and sword-swallowing—which might be classified as sports, we see this *siddhi*. In the nineteenth and early twentieth century there was a game which involved the ducking of bullets. Some of the great heroes of this pastime, it was said, became refractory to bullets through the power of their minds.

George Blanda, at 45, continues to amaze us. Sam Snead is a moneywinner on the PGA tour at the age of 61 and still has that famous swing. Percy Cerutty, one of the great track coaches and physical culturists of all time, is highly active at 79. Bernard McFadden parachuted into the Seine and the Thames on his 85th and 86th birthdays. Where will it all end?

11. Androgyny; ability to change sex; the 32 male and 32 female signs of the perfect Buddha.	Balance of the "male" and "female" characteristics.
12. Precognition, prophecy, retrocognition, time travel.	Freedom from tyranny of past, present or future; closeness to the Eternal; freedom from this game; psychic mobility
13. Clairaudience	Access to the inner worlds, the Music of the Spheres, the Omkar.
14. Telepathy, clairvoyance.	Freedom from the tyranny of the five senses.
15. Synaesthesia.	Freedom from the ordinary perceptual constancies, an unfettered mind.
16. Psychokinesis; moving objects at a distance through psychic power.	Mastery of the mind and emotions, will power.

Many male athletes, even in the fiercest sports, have a strikingly feminine aspect, contrary to the old macho cliche. Freed from the need to prove themselves in this regard they can allow a wider range of feeling and perceptions. This expansion of awareness through the dropping of defenses has been pointed out by various psychologists and sociologists of sport.

The David Meggesey incident described above is an instance of this. Meggyesey claims he made many tackles because he could anticipate the moves of the other team's running backs: somehow he knew what they would do an instant before they did it. A tennis instructor told me that the same kind of precognition has come to him during tennis games.

Bobby Jones often heard a melody as he played and sometimes used it to give a rhythm to his swing. The sound of crickets or a subtle ringing sometimes comes to golfers in the stillness of their concentration. Roscoe Newman, a retired Navy Captain tells about times when he was learning to fly, when he would "climb over the haze into a different world above five thousand feet and roll and loop until pleasantly pooped." During these flights he would "synchronize vocally, in song, with the vibrations and noise frequencies around me to come up with all the voice parts of a great choral group and/or the various instruments of a large orchestral assembly. There was absolutely no discord in the music I heard. Every part and tone was crystal clear, true, properly amplified and in unison."

An incredible power of communication often develops between members of a team—between a quarterback and wide receiver for example—where one can anticipate the moves of the other. Skiers tell about their sensing a comrade's danger or distress on the slopes. Ocean divers and skydivers have told me the same kind of stories.

This crossing of the senses sometimes occurs in golf. (I have described the state in *Golf in the Kingdom,* in a chapter entitled "The Pleasures of Practice," pp 171-72.)

Brodie described this power in the same *Intellectual Digest* article: "I would have to say that such things seem to exist—or emerge when your state of mind is right. It has happened to me dozens of times. An intention carries a force, a thought is connected with an energy that can stretch itself out in a pass play or a golf shot or a thirty foot jump shot in basketball. I've seen it happen too many times to deny it." It is a legendary power among certain pool and billiard players, among golfers, and in archery and target shooting.

17. Feats of extraordinary strength and endurance as with the *Lung Gom* walkers who, it is claimed, can walk for weeks without stopping through the mountains of Tibet.

Psychic strength and endurance.

A 26 mile marathon run at close to a five minute mile pace. Extraordinary moments of strength in weight lifting competition.

BIBLIOGRAPHY

ASSAGIOLI, Roberto, *The Act of Will*. New York: Viking, 1973.
————, *Psychosynthesis*. New York: Viking, 1971.
BANNISTER, Roger, *Four-Minute Mile*. New York: Dodd, Mead, 1955.
CERUTTY, Percy Wells, *Be Fit! or Be Damned!* London: Pelham, 1968.
————, *Middle Distance Running*. Los Altos, California: Tafnews, 1964.
————, *Sport Is My Life*. London: Stanley Paul, 1966.
————, *Success in Life and Sports*. London: Pelham, 1967.
DAUMAL, Rene, *Mount Analogue,* tr. Roger Shattuck. San Francisco: City Lights.
ELDENKRAIS, Moshe, *Awareness Through Movement*. New York: Harper & Row, 1972
ING, Gia-F, and H. Wilkerson, *Tai-Chi, a Way of Centering*. New York: Macmi , 1969.
GALLW   W. Timothy, *The Inner Game of Tennis*. New York: Random House, 1974.
HENDERSON, Joseph L., *Run Gently, Run Long*. Mountain View, California: Runner's World, 1974.
HUANG, Al Chung-liang, *Embrace Tiger, Return to Mountain*. Moab, Utah: Real People Press, 1973.
IYENGAR, B.K., *Light on Yoga*. New York: Schocken, 1966.
KEEN, Sam, *Beginnings without End*. New York: Harper & Row, 1975.
KRAMER, Joel, *The Passionate Mind*. Millbrae, California: Celestial Arts, 1974.
LEONARD, George, *The Ultimate Athlete*. New York: Viking, 1975.
LINDBERGH, Charles A., *The Spirit of St. Louis*. New York: Scribner's, 1953.
MURPHY, Michael, *Golf in the Kingdom*. New York: Viking, 1972.
ROZAK, Theodore, *Unfinished Animal*. New York: Harper & Row, 1975.
RUSH, Anne Kent, *Getting Clear: Body Work for Women*. New York: Random House/Bookworks, 1973.
SATPREM, *Sri Aurobindo, or the Adventure of Consciousness,* tr. Tehmi. New York: Harper & Row, 1974.
SOBEL, David, and Faith Hornbacher, *An Everyday Guide to Your Health*. New York: Grossman, 1973.
TOHEI, Koichi, *Aikido in Daily Life*. San Francisco: Japan Publications, 1966.